ON
CREATION

Religion
and Science
in Dialogue

WALTER
KLAIBER

Translated by Randi H. Lundell

Abingdon Press
Nashville

ON CREATION

RELIGION AND SCIENCE IN DIALOGUE

This book is printed on acid-free paper.

Library of Congress Cataloging-in-Publication Data

Klaiber, Walter.
  [Schöpfung. English]
  On Creation : religion and science in dialogue / Walter Klaiber ; translated by Randi H. Lundell.
    p. cm.
  Includes bibliographical references (p.   ) and index.
  ISBN 978-0-687-46687-0 (binding: pbk./trade pbk. : alk. paper)
    1. Bible. O.T. Genesis I-XI—Criticism, interpretation, etc. 2. Bible. O.T. Genesis I-XI—Theology. 3. Creation. I. Title.
  BS1235.52.K6213 2010
  231.7′652—dc22

                            2010012472

© Vandenhoeck & Ruprecht GmbH & Co. KG, Walter Klaiber: Schöpfung. Urgeschichte und Gegenwart, 1. Aufl., Göttingen, 2005.

All Scripture quotations are from the Luther Bible, revised edition 1984, published by the Deutsche Bibelgesellschaft, Stuttgart, 1999 (Lutherbibel, revidierter Text 1984, © Deutsche Bibelgesellschaft, Stuttgart).

10 11 12 13 14 15 16 17 18 19—10 9 8 7 6 5 4 3 2 1
MANUFACTURED IN THE UNITED STATES OF AMERICA

CONTENTS

II. POWER AND HISTORY—
THE FIRST STEPS (4:1–6:4)

III. LAW AND GRACE—
THE CRISIS (6:5–9:17)

IV. VARIETY AND CONFUSION—
THE EXPANSION (9:18–11:26)

CONCLUSION

FOREWORD

Where do we come from? Where are we going? These questions have occupied humanity since its beginning. Human beings are conscious of death—something that separates us from everything we know of the animal kingdom. As a result, the philosopher Martin Heidegger has characterized being human as "Being-unto-Death." Many people ask, "What comes after death?" Others are more interested in the question of how humankind will be able to continue.

People are just as intensely interested in the origins of humankind. In asking this question, people are not so much interested in their own personal destiny but in the question How did humanity begin? or How did the earth and the universe come into being? And the age-old question, assumed by many to be the basis for all of philosophy, is still being asked today: why is there something and not nothing?

The fact that these questions delve deeply into the problem of human existence can be seen by taking a look at the world of religion. There is scarcely a religion that does not have something to say about how the world came about. Myths tell of ancient times when the earth and humankind were created. The desire to know how this world and the people in it came into being is still of existential interest for us.

This is also true of secular society. Since we have learned that we live in an expanding universe and that this world had a beginning, cosmology has been at the center of public interest. Pictures of the universe from the Hubble telescope have been published with the heading "A Look at the Birth of the Universe." A somewhat difficult book to read by Stephen Hawking, *A Brief History of Time*, has become a bestseller and the question of whether before the Big Bang a God existed who had something to do with this history has become the subject of everyday conversation with taxi drivers. Indeed, the fact that the religious underpinnings of this question are not entirely lost is evidenced by the fact that there are numerous popular scientific books on the topic that display the word *creation* in their titles.

Likewise, in Germany it appears to be the case that the origins of human beings, and consequently the theme of evolution, have receded into the background. The "first three minutes of creation" appear to be of more interest than the question of the "missing link" between our primate ancestors and today's humans.

Against this background, what do the biblical accounts of the creation of the world and of humankind mean for the early history of humans? Are they just creation myths like many others, interesting to read but without any fundamental or practical meaning for today's struggles with these questions? Or do they point to a truth that is also relevant for us today?

To the extent of our knowledge, the question of creation occupied the people of Israel from very early times. The corresponding stories emerged gradually, partially in disagreement with the creation myths of the large and mighty neighboring cultures of the Babylonians and Egyptians. In the course of forming the canon, creation stories were then arranged at the front of the biblical writings, clearly addressing something essential about being human in this world.

Can this claim still be of any relevance today? How do we respond to the findings of science about the beginning and development of the cosmos, and about the origins of human beings? The end of the nineteenth and the first half of the twentieth centuries have been characterized by serious struggles over whether the Bible or Darwin was right, or, more simply stated, whether we humans were created by God or evolved from monkeys. When I was confronted with these questions as a schoolboy, it was customary and assumed in the Christian milieu in which I was raised that a person had to make a decision on this issue and that an understanding of the credibility of the Bible as the word of God meant saying no to the reports of science, in favor of those in the biblical accounts.

I am very thankful, however, that I now know Christians who have examined these alternatives and who have shown me a way in which faith and scientific thought are able to find common ground, even with regard to the story of creation. In the second half of the last century this conviction has consequently gained a foothold, at least in Europe, in the thinking of many evangelical theologians, as well as in the teachings of the Catholic Church. As a result, there has been a mostly peaceful albeit disconnected coexistence of two very different levels of dialogue as to the truth. This has changed in the last century, in which more intensive discussions have taken place between theology and science as a result of questions raised by cosmology.

What this means for the interpretation of the biblical early history is, however, pursued less frequently. In the following book I would therefore like to attempt an interpretation of Genesis 1–11, which raises these questions. I am very conscious of the fact that I am not a scholar of Old Testament exegesis or a specialist in questions of modern cosmology, nor am I a biologist. Nevertheless, I am still making the attempt as a result of the response to a casual disclosure of my yearlong reflections dabbling with this theme, which has given me the confidence to pursue it. Perhaps it takes an amateur who in working together with pastors and teachers of religion, and also interested nontheologians, is able to provide helpful suggestions for an interpretation of these chapters of the Bible.

I would like to thank Dr. Jörg Barthel for his thorough advice with regard to the Old Testament questions. He also designed two tables for use here.

I would like to thank my wife for the inception of this book because of her interest in the topic and our intense discussions of scientific questions. I am also grateful to her for her support in many other respects.

I would especially like to thank my former secretary, Mrs. Barbara Schieker, whose efforts made the appearance of this book on schedule possible despite my illness and my transition into retirement.

I submit this book in the hope that I will be able to impart to my readers something of the advancement in knowledge and insight into faith that I received through my work on the interpretation of ancient history and the questions that occupy science today.

Walter Klaiber

Tübingen
June 2005

INTRODUCTION

For today's reader it is almost self-evident that a book such as the Bible should begin with the sentence "In the beginning, God created heaven and earth." We expect such a book to talk about the creation of the world and of humankind, and to relate their early history. However, the fact that it is not obvious that this kind of text would provide the foundation for a religious book is evident by taking a look at the Qur'an. Moreover, the fact that we do know something about the development of the Pentateuch gives us reason to suspect that what we now know as the first five books of Moses (Pentateuch) did not include the early history at the beginning of the transmission process. In the course of the last twenty years the consensus that the process of transmission was seamless has been shaken and there is now a multitude of new and old models vying with one another to establish a history of the transmission of the Pentateuch.[1] However, it is true that in Israel the tradition of the founding fathers (of Israel) and excerpts from the Exodus from Egypt were the primary center of concern and consequently led to the first collection of stories. Later, at the end of the period of the kings—and perhaps even earlier—the first written collection of stories about the creation of humankind and its early history appeared. The backbone of this collection is to be found in Genesis 2:4-11, 9, and according to the early research includes, for example, some of the texts attributed to the Jahwist. However, many today contest the existence of such a source document threading its way through the entire Pentateuch.[2] In particular, an original connection between the Jahwist account in the early history and the Jahwist story line, beginning with Genesis 12:1-4, is rejected by many of today's exegetes. The basis for this is the observation that these two texts have no references in common and that in the original history the existence of people as sedentary farmers is clearly distinguished from the nomadic existence of Israel's forefathers in the stories of the patriarchs and in Exodus.[3]

However, most researchers accept the existence of a consistent source document called the priestly writings (P) because the text reveals a specific interest in cultic questions. It begins with Genesis 1:1–2:3, continues in 5:1-32, can be clearly distinguished from other Jahwist or "early priestly" story lines in the story of the flood, comes to its first climax in the story of the covenant with Abraham in Genesis 17, and presumably ends with Deuteronomy 34:7-9.[4] The first version, the so-called basic writings of P, appeared around the end of the Exile period. It used a structure that was later employed during the postexilic period to transmit handed-down material about the early history of Israel, and was thus constructed, step-by-step, into the Pentateuch.

The resulting text challenges current interpretations in two ways:

1. The end product is a thick weave of different threads that remain distinct yet, when woven together, comprise an entirely different total picture; or—as one must perhaps say in light of the many passages—this text is like an artfully arranged quilt whose individual "blocks" readily reveal their different origins yet still blend together into a colorful whole. The exegete's task is therefore to try to understand the message of the text as a whole and to clarify it. However, he or she must also consider what the individual traditions and sources that have been interwoven are trying to say.
2. The incorporation of the early history as the first part of the book of Genesis, and subsequently as part of the entire Pentateuch, meant that this tradition became part of the Torah. *Torah* is the name for the first five books of the Bible. The Hebrew word *tora* means "law." Greek-speaking Jews translated it using the word *nomos*, which means "law." The New Testament also uses this word to refer to the Pentateuch. The concept contains the core of many misunderstandings—something that would

happen if the Pentateuch were to be viewed primarily as a law book. However, the collection of laws are embedded into a story line that not only provides a framework for the stories but is also an integrated part of the Torah—that is, the fundamental wisdom of God for God's people.

This is also the case for the historical texts that have a universal, all-embracing horizon. What is said here about the creation of the world and of humans, about transgressions and threats to human existence, about humanity's endangered relationship to God and God's promise to be loyal to humanity should nevertheless be viewed as a valid geographical marker and a trustworthy signifier for all of humankind, as it offers the perspective of faith in the God of Israel.

Thus, the Jewish or Christian interpreters of the early history or prehistory are not just like any other interested reader of primitive myths who asks questions about the existence and worldview of the people who transmitted these stories. They are also, as can be seen by the enduring message of this text, asking questions that are relevant for us today—questions that ask how these texts relate to competing explanations regarding the beginning of the world and of humanity as well as how these texts relate to the roots of many fundamental anthropological conditions such as shame, guilt, aggression, and the power of hubris. However, before we ask these questions, we will first allow the individual stories to speak from their own moment in time.[5]

CHAPTER ONE

CREATION AND FALL—
THE BEGINNING (1:1–3:24)

A basic assumption of biblical scholarship is that two versions of creation are combined into Genesis 1–3, each portraying the creation of the world and of humankind but each employing a different method and taking a different perspective. However, each version should be treated individually before one can explore the similarities.

1. The Creation of the World in Seven Days (1:1–2:3)

The first account of creation stems from a document that ranks among the most important in the religious literature of the world. It is characterized by an extremely dense and carefully constructed narrative. Old Testament interpreters consider this document to mark the beginning of the priestly writings (P), as has already been briefly outlined in the introduction.

The story gives evidence of two different structures.[1] In the foreground, the division of creation is divided into six days, after which God rests on the seventh day. God's activity corresponds to the activity of humans and to the Jewish tradition for dividing up the week. This division is marked by the stereotypical formula "and there was evening and morning on the Xth day." However, woven into this structure is a second narrative that is marked by the formula "and God spoke." In this structure, eight works of creation are divided into six days of creation.[2]

The narrative begins with a very simple sentence: "In the beginning, God created the heavens and the earth." According to the majority of scholarly interpretations, this sentence serves as a kind of heading summarizing everything that happens between verses 3 and 31. There is another plausible interpretation that says that verse 1 is a subordinate clause to verse 2 (or also to verse 3). The key to this interpretation is that verse 1 does not talk about a first act of creation by which the earth is created in the manner described in verse 2. "Heaven and earth" is a formula that encompasses everything, including, to be sure, the ordered world, but verse 2 does not mention it; the creating activity of God begins only with verse 3. The formula "in the beginning" does not mark an originating historical date but indicates "a fundamental event . . . in which God vouches for everything that happens afterward."[3]

The way in which the narrative talks about God is of great importance. God is present without any preconditions and is introduced as the sole and sovereign agent. In contrast to other religious myths, the biblical world does not involve theogony—that is, it does not contain a story about the birth of, or the creation of, the gods.

An aspect of the sovereignty of God is contained in the Hebrew, which we translate as "to create." In the Hebrew Bible, *bara'* is the term reserved for God's actions and is employed in contrast to the verb "to make" whenever God's creating activity involves something that is not crafted from available materials but occurs without any preexisting conditions.[4] However, verse 2 suggests that the Old Testament is not speaking of *creatio ex nihilo*, creation from nothing.[5]

It is difficult to say what the preexisting conditions for creation are as they are depicted in verse 2. Does it describe an "original substance" from which God created the world? What meaning should we attach to these preconditions? Or should we say that whatever it was, it did not provide any conditions for an ordered creation that could accommodate animals and human beings?

Whatever was present at the beginning when God created heaven and earth, three propositions are possible. (1) The earth was desolate and empty. The Hebrew word *tohuwabohu* used here retains its original meaning when translated into the German: total chaos, completely uninhabitable, nothingness.[6] (2) Darkness lay over the waters. *Tehom* (Luther: "the depths") denotes the formless body of water of the early period; it was covered by an impenetrable darkness that is not defined in contrast to light but represents a kind of dark nothingness. Although there is no relationship between the idea of *tehom* and the Babylonian dragon goddess Tiamat from whom, according to the Babylonian saga, Marduk created the world, the original body of water and the attending darkness were not just physical concepts but mythical categories. As motifs they are connected to ancient oriental myths of creation that begin with the formula "as not yet . . ." or that take pains to first portray the negative background against which the world was created. However, the biblical story reveals the underlying conditions of the power of its narrative and "emphasizes the conditions for creation as occurring from nothing."[7] (3) God moves over the waters. This sentence is the most difficult to understand as well as to translate. The meaning of the verb, which Luther translated as "hover," is not entirely clear and contains a participle that is most closely translated as "wavering." The exact meaning of *ruach 'elohim* used here is also open to question: "spirit," "wind," or "the breath of God"? Perhaps this phrase does not mean an act of God's creation but rather describes the original condition prior to creation—namely, in the world not yet created by God there was order, but it consisted of a not-yet-arranged, oscillating, formless energy.

The portrayal of the original conditions for creation in verse 2 also contains its own unique ambivalence. In it something is depicted that predates God's activity of creating, but this "something" is a "nothing" and contains no creative potential; it is a pre-something that will be engaged by God's creating activity.

The First Day of Creation

Verses 3-5 describe the first act of creation occurring on the first day of creation. In a very matter-of-fact way it says: "And God said: let there be light. And there was light." Light, the epitome of life-giving energy, springs from God's creating words. There is no better interpretation of this sentence than what is written in Haydn's oratorio *The Creation*. The powerful emission of energy

3

and harmony in the creation of light is communicated impressively in the *fortissimo subito* of the chorus.

The fact that light is created before the sun and the moon is significant. On the one hand, it serves to demythologize and not to deify the sun and the moon, which were of great importance for the religions of the world. On the other hand, it reveals an almost modern knowledge of the original meaning of life-giving energy, which goes well beyond the phenomenon of optically visible electromagnetic rays. The energy for life is only unleashed through God's word—an idea that is not unique to the Orient, but nevertheless is not encountered very often.[8]

Special care is taken to emphasize that God regards the light as "good." In this context, "good" means according to its purpose and serving the desired goal. Light is the engine of creation.

In a remarkable way the story of the narrative of God's sovereign creating activity through his word marks a new emphasis: "God separated the light from the darkness." This appears to be a very different description of God's creating activity: from an undifferentiated original condition comes the creative contrast of light and dark. In modern terms, out of an "original (state of) entropie" of an original singularity, God creates the condition of energy that subsequently sets everything in motion.

Here we encounter the fundamental tension belonging to the first creation account. Next to the depiction of God's creation through his word there are reports of how God shapes and creates the world through his actions. Many interpreters would like to differentiate a completely literary, factual report of God's deeds apart from that of God's word, which is dominant.[9] Yet, no matter how the early history of the text may have emerged, we still have the task of interpreting the existing tension in light of the final form of the story.

It is interesting to note that in both of the first acts of creation the activity of God is described as "dividing" (between light and dark, the water below and the heavens above the firmament), and, in fact, the third act of creation also describes the activity of dividing the seas from firm land.

Accordingly, a main tenet of ancient oriental thought on creation has been incorporated: the division of polar opposites such as heaven and earth, or water and land, from an undifferentiated primal situation is a basic element of the origin of the world in its present form. In Egypt and Mesopotamia this was often portrayed in mythological terms (e.g., division of an androgynous divine pair or separation of the dragon goddess Tiamat), and the accounts from the priestly writings do this with almost scientific precision. The element of dividing during creation is also underscored by the fact that in all three cases the creative act is accomplished through God's "naming" of the newly created reality (compare Table 1). The act of "defining" is thus part of God's creation; it is a "determination" about what comes into being and its order and arrangement, which have arisen from the unordered and thus unformed original condition.

Although light is created, darkness is not excluded from the world as a whole. Light and darkness are differentiated so that from the impenetrable and threatening darkness of night there is the benefit of a contrast between day and night. Since it is named and given limitations, the darkness loses its threat and, in the opposition between light and darkness, light has the upper hand as a result of its creative potential.

With the division of light and darkness there is also the first day; the rhythm of time is a mark of the created world and not of the eternity that encompasses it. Whether the teller of this story has portrayed it as a twenty-four-hour day is a futile question. Sun and moon, which are designated to divide day and night, have not been created yet. Thus, the time for "day" has basically been prescribed, but it still cannot be measured in today's terms.

The Second Day of Creation

Verses 6-8 describe the second act of creation as taking place precisely on the second day of creation. The text says: "God said: let there be an expanse between the waters to separate water from water." Luther's translation of "expanse" is not indigenous to the German language but is closer to the Latin for "firmament." It means something like "the dome of heaven's vault" (possibly of hammered metal). Its function consists in dividing and limiting the water from causing a flood. What is meant is shown in the first narrative. God "makes" heaven's vault and as a result a concept is employed that does not avoid an analogy to human handiwork, dividing the water underneath heaven's vault (a type of primal ocean) from the water on the upper half of heaven's vault, namely, heaven's ocean. This process corresponds to a widespread idea in the ancient world that said through the creation of heaven's vault a space was created for all creatures in the area between the floodwaters of the depths and the floodwaters of the heavens (see Abb. 1).[10]

According to Genesis 7:11, one of the sections of the story of the flood in P, things escalate to catastrophic proportions when the fountain of the depths and the channels of heaven's vault open up and the ordered world is again threatened by the chaos of undivided floodwaters.

The firmament is named heaven, which denotes a phenomenon of nature ("sky") and not the dwelling place of God ("heaven").

The Third Day of Creation

Verses 9-13 describe the third and fourth act of creation as occurring on the third day of creation. Both acts of creation talk about the earth as a place fit for life. First, God's creating word commands that the water should collect at a particular place and, accordingly, dry land appears. There is no report of facts, just an announcement—"and it was so"—and the important reference that God names the "dry" places "earth" and the body of water the "sea." Thus, the final basic division and definition are completed that makes the world a place capable of sustaining life. The earth is no more "empty and void"; it is now a "firm land" and has become a "habitat." The seas have also emerged from the limitless and wild primal flood state to having firm boundaries. "Water" that was previously a threatening primal element is now introduced into the household of creation as a life-giving element. And that is also good and serves a good purpose for all that has been created.

The threefold division contained in the first three acts of creation serves to create the living space for future creatures: the expanse of time, the division of space into upper and lower, and the security of a fundamental "here" occur in these three acts.[11]

Immediately upon the appearance of dry land there is a new command: the command to the earth to bring forth plants. Here again instead of a report of facts there is the announcement of completion. However, this time it is not the brief formula "and it was so" but the extended repetition of the original command: "and the earth brought forth." Here a new dimension is revealed with regard to the creating activity of God—namely, creation also happens when what is created brings forth new creations of its own.

Two observations are worth noting: (1) At this juncture, the narrative takes on a kind of scientific tone. Seed-bearing grasses and weeds are carefully distinguished from fruit-bearing trees. For the first time it is also stressed that everything developed "according to its kind." (2) The plant kingdom is seen as very "close to the earth." Thus, the third and fourth acts of creation are collected into one day of creation and yet still come before the creation of the sun and moon. "Life" in the narrow sense first begins for the priestly writers with the kingdom of the animals (v. 20). Plants are "nourishment" for animals and man (v. 29) and belong to the basis of life, as they serve the created earth. Everything that is good and that serves life is the goal of God's creation.

The Fourth Day of Creation

Verses 14-19 tell of the fourth day and the fifth act of creation. We have already referred to how unusual it is that here the stars are named for the first time. God's commanding word gives them their precise definition. There will be light in the firmament to divide day and night, which serves as a sign of orientation for space and time—especially for festive seasons—and which defines days and years in their course in time, and, in various ways, lights up the earth.

The report of the deed described in the above account depicts God once more as the Creator who "makes" what should be and who assigns to everything its appropriate place. The familiar picture of the divine watchmaker would be the closest to this portrayal. This is precision work. God makes two large lights: the largest defines the day and the smaller one the night, but their names are not mentioned. The concepts of sun and moon appear to be so strongly associated with the veneration of the day (or with that of the night star) in the form of gods that here, where it has to do with their function in God's creation, they not are mentioned.

The same is true for the stars. The meaning of the heavenly bodies is not displaced. Sun and moon rule the day and the night, lighting up the earth, and essentially complete what was already defined in the first work of creation; they divide the light from the darkness (v. 18; compare v. 14, day and night). However, their meaning is relative. They have an important, clearly defined function. Here in the first work of creation we already have a distinction between astrology and astronomy—and that is also good in God's eyes.

The Fifth Day of Creation

Now the earth is a suitable space for living creatures. Verses 20-23 portray how, on the fifth day, living creatures were created to occupy spaces not suitable for people—namely, the waters of the ocean and the air of the sky. In a very moving account, we have a description of the fullness of life that will emerge: "Let the water teem with living creatures." A multitude of various forms of animal life both in the water and in the sky is described. And for the second time while reporting the deed, the narrator uses the celebratory formula "and God created." The emergence of "living creatures"—that is, of animals that breathe, eat, and procreate—is a new step in God's creative work and is intentionally marked by the word *bara'* (to create). Moreover, hidden in the term translated as "living creature"—the Hebrew word *nephesh*—is something that is often translated as "soul." It denotes that everything living carries in it a "living breath," so that with this word all animals and people can be collected together under a common, overarching concept.

From among the fullness of life, one species is emphasized: the great sea monsters (Luther: "the great whales"), creatures that were feared and worshiped as divine beings. These were also God's creatures that belonged to a large animal park, created by God so that he could play with them (Ps. 104:26).

This new section of God's creating activity also includes the words of blessing that he speaks in which he says that what he has created is good: "Be fruitful and multiply." It is the designation of the earth, and with it the ocean and the space between the earth and the firmament, as a living space for many animals.

These words of blessing also very well illustrate what a blessing is according to the Old Testament: a promise of life in all of its fullness.[12]

The Sixth Day of Creation

Verses 24-31 tell of God's work on the sixth day. It is the most comprehensive account in the series and includes the seventh and eighth acts of creation. The creation of animals and humans is relayed in close connection to each other. There is nothing to indicate that this is a provisional measure, since the seventh day of creation has to be reserved for God's day of rest. Because of its emphasis on the special case of humans, this account knows more about the creaturely connection between the existence of animals and the being of humans than many apologists of biblical creationism would like to admit.

With the story of the creation of land animals, we encounter once more the interlocking of two aspects of the act of creation. The command to create is: "Let the land produce" (v. 24). The creative potential of what is already created is part of the creative will of God. In the narrative account, the formula "and it was so" is then followed by the words "God made." God's "making" and the bringing forth of the earth are two aspects of the same creative process. In the individual accounts, there is a differentiation between wild animals and domestic animals that is to include mammals, whereas the rest is "vermin." In each account it is again stressed that everything is created "according to its kind." Hybrid creatures, which are viewed primarily in Egypt as representatives of the divine, are not a part of God's creation.

Although this work is found to be good, God does not bless the animals belonging to the land; that blessing is reserved for humankind. Are the animals included in this blessing or should they be seen as competing with humans for the same living space, and are they not intended to multiply and fill the earth in the same way? That remains an open question. In any case, the story reaches its climax with the creation of humankind.

This is introduced by a distinctly new element. The formula "and God said" is the result of God's challenge to himself that is conveyed primarily by the phrase in the plural: "Let us make

9

men." We find similar plural sayings in Babylonian myths, which are, however, sayings decreed by a divine council, in which case the plural is understandable. In the Old Testament context it is arranged so that either God is incorporated into the "sons of God" (heavenly beings) (compare 3:22; 11:7; 1 Kings 22:19-22; Isa. 6:7) or the exhortative plural is the majestic plural, namely, the plural that is used to give advice *(deliberationis)* and that functions in the polemical superiority of a polytheistic creation myth to "express the free decision of the one and only God (of Israel), who alone is able to bring creation to life."[13]

A rich history of interpretation that has been the subject of much speculation has produced the phrase "according to our image and likeness," which has then been repeated as the complete statement "And God created [humankind] in his image."

The consensus of modern interpretation is that it does not mean that humans resemble the external image of God. Neither walking upright nor the ability to think or to make decisions makes human beings into the likeness of God. Parallels in the ancient Orient indicate that "God's likeness" describes a relationship or a function. In Egypt and Mesopotamia kings are the representatives of God who exert complete authority over and dominate their subjects.[14] In Genesis 1:26 the human beings' likeness to God is the basis for their ability to dominate. However, this dominion is not about individuals ruling over other humans, but rather over the animals. Humans are the representatives of God and embody his "yes" to life (compare 9:6); they are the representatives and regents of his life-creating lordship (compare v. 28; Ps. 8:5-7). Therefore, the record stresses once more the express act of God's "creating" humans in the image of God and the creation of man and woman in relation to each other. Some early androgynous idea of God is not implied here, and neither is any likeness an indication of something divine in the relationship between man and woman.[15] However, it clearly establishes that all human beings have a part in the worth, power, and responsibility that is attributed to them as part of their divine likeness. The ancient ideology of royalty was thus "democratized" while at the same time "the person as a species was royalized."[16]

Empowerment and responsibility are emphasized in the words of blessing that God speaks over humanity.[17] Here again it has to do with the fullness of life and with the empowerment to utilize the resources of the earth: "Be fruitful and increase in number; fill the earth"—the earth as a whole is thus dedicated to humans—"to subdue it . . . and rule over every living creature." The words that are used to describe human dominion are taken entirely from language used for ruling and dominance. In our postmodern shock over this, we should not forget that at the time these verses were written wild animals were not included under the rubric of "endangered species" but were seen as a real threat. However, the understanding of lordship or rule that is applied to the divine image emphasizes the responsibility of a ruler who intends to take care of his creation and protect it (compare Ps. 72). The close relationship between the ancient oriental ideology of lordship and the image of the shepherd, to which also belongs the metaphor of "dominate and oppress" (without the negative connotation), shows why humans are made in God's likeness: they are the "shepherds of the animals."[18] The apportionment of food in the next verse assigns fruits and seeds for humans but limits the animals to grass, making clear that in this concept of lordship and dominance there is no place for exploitation and destruction, but only for a kind of supremacy of humankind that allows room for all other living things.

It is important to make clear that the creation of human beings in the image of God is one of the biblical motifs that carries a potential for meaning beyond what is conveyed in the text, and which is first included in the history of the scholarship. The verse concerning humanity's likeness to God contains a beneficial tension because it not only describes the divine connection of people in their likeness to God but also in their relationship to God. People as representatives of God are also regents of the earth—not so that they can take God's place, but that through their relationship to God they can hold a place open for God in creation.

Here there is also a marked difference from the Sumarian and Babylonian creation myths, which seem otherwise to have many correlations. These stories clearly indicate that humankind was created to take on the job of the lower gods in serving the higher gods.[19] However, the biblical creation account makes no reference to this anywhere. People are not created to be in relationship to God in order to serve him, but to be his partner in this world,

11

which, however, is a task that remains indissolubly connected to him as Creator. Thus, God gives not only a picture of the creation of humans at the end of the sixth day, but also a view of all that is created. He pronounces that it is "very good." "The world is created by God for the purpose of life!"[20] And everything created is "very good" because it serves life. But that is precisely the function of the job of humankind's lordship, "for in the event of creation God establishes the ongoing continuation of the entire created world for the benefit of all created life!"[21]

The Seventh Day of Creation

Genesis 2:1 concludes with an interim remark: God completed his work. Heaven and earth "in its vast array" and everything that belongs to it has been created. Verse 2 repeats this statement: God completes his work and carries it further; he rests on the seventh day from all of his labors. The story gains a specific Jewish tone as a result of this very unique motif originating from the priestly creation account. Of course, the concept of "Sabbath" is not present, but it is clear that here the Jewish day of rest is described as based in creation (compare Exod. 20:11).

Just as on the fifth day of creation the animals of the water and the air were blessed, and on the sixth day of creation people as representatives of the creatures of the earth were blessed and sent forth in order to live out their God-given fullness of life, so now God also blesses the seventh day as a day of rest.[22] Not just the doing, but also the allowing, is blessed and carries with it creative potential and the promise of the fullness of life. In order to protect this day God "blesses" it—that is, he keeps it for himself in order to retain it for humankind. The day of rest is also still expressly connected to the "making" as well as to the "creating" activity of God.

The fact that God's creating activity culminates in rest makes God himself the goal of creation. Thus, although the creation story appears to be anthropocentric in Genesis 1:26-31, it is actually theocentric. God does not appear in the midst of his creation. The day of rest creates a free space for him and is an expression of his freedom in relation to his creation in which he is not limited like some kind of principle but stands over it both in the act of creating as well as at rest.[23] The fact that the seventh day of creation does not end with the "daily formula" appears to indicate that here time is open and a piece of eternity breaks in.

This gives the entire story a unique and productive ambivalence. On the one hand, it says that God has perfected heaven and earth and everything that belongs to him (2:1); God does not allow creation to remain unfinished. On the other hand, the motif of calm on the seventh day indicates the unspoken possibility of a further week of creation and is thus capable of connecting with the idea of a *creatio continua*, the ongoing creation and preservation of the world (compare Ps. 104). According to the witness of the priestly writings, this motif refers to a decisive encounter of God with the world, namely, the revelation on Mount Sinai for the salvation of God's people.[24] In Exodus 24:16 the seven-day motif appears again where the "Tent of Meeting" and the altar consecrate as holy the place in which God will dwell in the midst of his people (Exod. 29:45). According to the priestly account, the "dwelling" of the creating God in the midst of the Israelites is the goal of the story of God and his relationship to humanity and to his people.

Most translations and interpretations find in verse 4a a summarizing signature of the first creation story, since the formula of the *toledot* (meaning witness; history of origins) of heaven and earth corresponds exactly to the language used in the priestly writings (compare 5:1; 10:1; 11:10-27; 25:12, and so on). However, in all of the examples the formula comes at the beginning of the list of accomplishments, particularly in a story that establishes its fate. Thus, I am inclined to agree with more recent interpreters that an editor influenced by the priestly writings inserted this formula in 2:4 as a heading for the second, in his view, clearly more comprehensive account.[25]

2. Preliminary Observations on the First Creation Account

Before we go any further, we should pause briefly and try to understand the unique quality of this creation account. We cannot proceed without comparing it to other creation stories in the Old Testament and the ancient oriental world. In addition, the challenges that science conveys both to our understanding and to personal encounters with statements contained in the passages should be kept in mind.

2.1 The Character and Message of the First Creation Account

Genesis 1:1–2:3 comprises a story. More precisely, this text is a report. Here we have a narrative that is both factual and matter-of-fact; it is an ordered and systematic account of the creation of the world. The seven-day schema and the subsequent eight acts of creation give the report a decided order, yet the weaving together of both of the main accounts prevents the narrative from appearing too schematic.

The core of the report features God's activity. Next to creating and arranging through his word there is the element of craftsmanship or of "making," which is also connected with the ability of the earth to bring forth plants and animals at God's behest.

The narrative becomes more detailed and animated the more it has to do with the creation of living creatures. A clear caesura is marked by God's challenge to himself: "Let us make [humankind] in our own image" (1:26). Thus, the creation of humans is not merely the result, but the high point of the creation story. However, this climax is embedded in God's entire creation and as a result the charge for humans to rule receives limitations. It is the resting of God (and not the creation of human beings) through which creation will be perfected (2.2). The motif of God's rest means that God's creating activity is finished, but it does not mean that it is "created." God's resting hides the unexpressed potential of creative guardianship and preservation of what has been created.

The message of the narrative is clear: God has made this earth capable of sustaining life. It is a blessed place in which humans, as the bearers of that blessing and as God's representatives, have an important task. All of that is also God's work; his sovereign initiative alone is to be thanked for this world's development and for its very existence. As a result of the clarity—almost monotony—with which this is told, the plain, modest report carries an almost hymnic quality.

2.2 The Connection with Other Old Testament Passages on Creation[26]

To glorify God as the Creator appears to be the oldest and most basic way of dealing with the theme of creation in Israel. Thus, in the Psalms, the preexilic period is primarily the struggle of Yahweh against chaos, which the flooding of the seas represents and primeval dragons personify, and is emphasized as the paramount act of God for the creation and preservation of the world. This clearly borrows content from Babylonian and Canaanite myths and refers to ideas that also are likely behind Genesis 1:2.

An example is Psalm 89:9-15 (8-15 in some translations):

> O Lord God Almighty, who is like you?
>> You are mighty, O Lord, and your faithfulness surrounds you.
> You rule over the surging sea;
>> when its waves mount up, you still them.
> You crushed Rahab like one of the slain;
>> with your strong arm you scattered your enemies.
> The heavens are yours, and yours also the earth;
>> you founded the world and all that is in it.
> You created the north and the south;
>> Tabor and Hermon sing for joy at your name.
> Your arm is endued with power;
>> your hand is strong, your right hand exalted.
> Righteousness and justice are the foundation of your throne;
>> love and faithfulness go before you.
> Blessed are those who have learned to acclaim you,
>> who walk in the light of your presence, O Lord.

It is interesting to note that in this text, next to the highly mythological motif of the fight against the primeval dragon (compare also Isa. 51:9; Ps. 74:12), the mention of justice and right as forming the supports for God's throne are introduced as fundamentals of creation and the basis for human community.[27]

The fact that the world stands firm and does not wobble, and that the earth's foundations reach above the sea, belongs to the basic elements of thanks to God in the Psalms (Ps. 78:69; 93:1; 96:10; 104:5). Accordingly, the themes of creation and preservation of the earth are strongly interwoven. From this basic knowledge, Psalm

104 unfolds with the glorification of the Creator in which are
blended together a lauded account of creation as a place for life on
earth (vv. 5-9) as well as an astonishing glimpse into the arranging
of all created life (v. 10). If one views the text more closely, two
theological concepts concerning creation are distinguishable in the
Psalms and in Wisdom literature: one sees in creation the actual
proof of the creating power of God against the background of a
world continually threatened by chaos (e.g., Ps. 93), while the other
emphasizes the elimination of chaos initially against the background of a well-ordered world (Gen. 1; Ps. 104; Spr. 8:29).[28]

The fact that the world was created through God's awesome
word is the Psalms' theme, which is chronologically placed in close
proximity to the priestly creation stories (Ps. 33:6; 148:5; compare
also 136:5-9; see also where Gen. 1:14-18 exhorts praise in connection with God's saving acts on behalf of Israel).

Quite apart from the psalmist, the reference to the creation of
heaven and earth is delivered by way of a formula that names the
God of Israel in his all-encompassing power. This can be found
with particular clarity in Deutero-Isaiah, where the motif places at
the forefront the dominance of the apparently powerless God of
Israel over all other gods, and God establishes his intention to create something new for his people (Jes. 40:26-31; 42:5; 44:24; 45:12;
48:12; in this regard the connection between creation and Exodus is
also significant. See Isa. 51:9-11; Ps. 77:17). However, although creation theology makes its appearance in the service of the message
of salvation for the future, in this connection it has to do with statements that function to summarize Genesis 1. For example, Isaiah
45:18:

> For this is what the LORD says,
>> he who created the heavens, he is God;
> he who fashioned and made the earth, he founded it;
>> he did not create it to be empty, but formed it to be inhabited.
> He says: I am the LORD and there is no other.

Thus, we have a remarkable situation where precisely the side of
divine activity that existed among the religions in Israel's environment served to identify the uniqueness of the God of Israel! For
example, one may compare Jonah 1:9, "I worship the LORD, the
God of heaven, who made the sea and the land"; or the letter of

Huram, the king of Tyre, in 2 Chronicles 2:12, "Blessed be the God of Israel, who made heaven and earth"; or the direct juxtaposition in Psalm 96:5 (1 Chron. 16:26), "For all the gods of the nations are idols, but the LORD made the heavens." Against this background, the formula becomes an important means of prayerful invocation, as for example in the prayer of Hezekiah (2 Kings 19:15; Isa. 37:16): "O LORD, God of Israel, enthroned between the cherubim, you alone are God over all the kingdoms of the earth. You have made heaven and earth" (compare Jer. 32:17; Neh. 9:6).

Thus, "the LORD who has made heaven and earth" is also the God in whose name we have the promise of help and blessing, as in Genesis 14:19, "Blessed be Abram by God Most High, Creator of heaven and earth"; or Psalm 115:15, "May you be blessed by the LORD, the Maker of heaven and earth" (connected with an impressive coupling of confession of the one, true God, which is comparable with the theology of blessing in Gen. 1); or Psalm 134:3, "May the LORD, the Maker of heaven and earth, bless you from Zion."

The confessions in Psalm 121:2 also belong here: "My help comes from the LORD, the Maker of heaven and earth"; or Psalm 124:8: "Our help is in the name of the LORD, the Maker of heaven and earth"; or more comprehensively in Psalm 146:5-7: "Blessed is he whose help is the God of Jacob, whose hope is in the LORD his God, the Maker of heaven and earth, the sea, and everything in them—the LORD, who remains faithful forever. He upholds the cause of the oppressed and gives food to the hungry. The LORD sets prisoners free." The latter verse states very emphatically that God's life-serving order in creation and his saving, creating activity within the human community complement each other.

The relationship among all of the traditions that have to do with the priestly accounts of creation is unique: the people whom God has created can expect help and blessing from the One who has blessed what he has created.

However, interpretations of the Old Testament do not agree on whether the theme of creation for the faith of Israel actually deserves the rank afforded to the creation story by virtue of its prominent place in today's canon. Scholars who are more oriented toward the historical development of the Old Testament are inclined to view this theme as a later, more marginal account,[29] whereas others who concern themselves with the entirety of the

Hebrew Bible see in it a central statement about the faith of Israel and about Old Testament theology.[30] Thus, the question also plays a role in the extent to which the Old Testament accounts are dependent upon the creation myths of the ancient oriental world.

2.3 The Relationship to Ancient Oriental Creation Myths[31]

For more than one hundred years the Old Testament research has concerned itself, to varying degrees, with the question of to what extent the biblical creation accounts and passages are dependent upon ancient oriental precursors. In short, the history of the research has led to a paradoxical conclusion.

On the one hand, there is detailed information in the many connections between the accounts. Understanding them is a tremendous help in understanding the biblical texts. The fact that a heavenly vault is part of the world's construction upon which the heavenly oceans are founded, and that the earth is set on pillars over the waters of the deep, explains a series of biblical statements. The mythical story from the Babylonian *Enuma Elish* of the fight of Marduk against the goddess Tiamat in the form of a dragon, which represents the oceans and the chaos that threatens life, and from whose divided body heaven and earth are formed, sheds light on the ideas that support Psalm 74:121 and 98:11, and possibly also Genesis 1:2. In addition, the creation of everything through the word of a creating god has an important parallel in Egyptian mythology and is clearly integrated into the polytheistic system of the Egyptian cosmos of deities.[32]

On the other hand, one enters another world if one reads the biblical stories on creation in light of the information on various ancient oriental myths. This is first of all because of the strict monotheistic tone of these stories. Ancient oriental creation myths are in large part theogony—that is, they tell of the gods' creation of the world and only later on, often in conjunction with a fatal disagreement between rival gods, do they tell of the coming into being of the cosmos and the creation of humankind.

There is no creation story in the ancient Orient that tells of the creation of the world systematically and with almost scientific precision, and in which the world develops step-by-step into a habitat for the various forms of life, as is the case in the priestly creation account. Not least, there is a serious difference with regard to the Babylonian creation myth's portrayal of the meaning of humanity. According to the *Enuma Elish*, people were created in order to relieve the work of the lesser gods who were in the service of the greater gods.[33] Human beings were never given dignity or even a name comparable to what they receive in the Genesis 1:26 account.

Nor does any Egyptian version even approximate the biblical portrayal. In the following quotation from *The Teaching for King Merikare* we have an ancient oriental text that comes closest to the priestly account:

> Well tended in mankind, the cattle of the gods;
> he made sky and earth for their sake;
> he subdued the water monster;
> he made breath for their noses to live.
> They are his images, which came from his body.
> He shines in the sky for their sake.
> He made for them plants and cattle, fowl and fish to feed them.
> He slew his foes, reduced his children, when they thought of making rebellions.
> He makes daylight for their sake; he sails by to see them.
> He has built his shrine around them; when they weep he hears.[34]

This is one of the few places in the Egyptian text in which a description of honor in the "image" of the gods not only applies to the king but to all humans. And although the appellation of "god" here means exclusively that of the sun god, the text also has something of a "monotheistic color," something closer to the biblical accounts than is the case for many other texts belonging to the background of the Old Testament.

However, the monotheism of the Hebrew Bible has been a recent point of discussion not only because it appears to be a later phenomenon of the Israelite history of religion,[35] but also because the "mosaic distinction" between the one, true God and false gods affords the case for religious intolerance and (abuse) of power.[36] What is important for our discussion is the observation that for monotheism the contrast between God and the world is constitutive, whereas the world of the gods of polytheism represents the principle that the world is "inherently structured, ordered, and

meaningful"[37] and therefore able, in and of itself, to explain its con-
tractions and anomalies.

As a matter of fact, at this point there are indications of a very
impressive and self-contained first account of creation that contains nothing of the hidden and dark sides that we encounter in the
created world. Even if the polytheistic creation myths of the
ancient world could offer no explanation for these phenomena,
there lies in what seem like almost abstruse stories indications of
problems between and among the gods! "The advantage of polytheism lies obviously with respect to the deeply contradictory actuality that here the world, as it is experienced in concrete terms, can
be traced back to the push-pull of various divine intentions."[38] The
monotheism of creation theology, however, describes God in his
sovereignty and freedom as standing opposite the world (and a
person is precisely "in his freedom, independence, and responsibility . . . an image of God").[39] It portrays God's activity also as a
categorical yes to his creation. Therefore, the question of theodicy,
which is completely ignored in the first creation story, is put to the
acid test of faith in one God who is the Creator of heaven and earth.

However, albeit in a very different way, the same question is still
being discussed in conversation with today's scientific observations and scientific method.

2.4 The Dialogue with Science

Despite the numerous connections between the first creation
story and ancient oriental myths, the differences are just as astonishing. The text represents a unique mixture of natural history and
theology, even for the worldview of its time. Of all of the comparable creation myths "only the biblical depiction of nature in general withstands comparison to the results of science."[40] The
creation story in Genesis 1 is like a "myth in the spirit of science,"
yielding something that would not be possible with other myths:
"a direct textual comparison with modern science."[41]

Such a comparison (such as in Hansjörg and Wolfgang
Hemminger) may refer to the gradual formation of heaven and
earth, the seas and firm land, and the forms of plants and animals,
as well as to the remarkable difference between the emergence of
primeval energy ("light") and the list of the stars, or to the close

connection between animals and people in the course of six days of creation. For a sympathetic reader it is impressive to note how many connecting points there really are; and as interpreters, one must exercise restraint so as not to introduce too much modern knowledge into the ancient texts themselves.[42]

Despite the similarities, the clear differences must also be acknowledged: the seven-day schema opposes scientific explanation, as does the order of the creation of plants before that of the stars. Any attempt to prove that the Bible has anticipated, although in a somewhat colorful way, knowledge of today's science is as misguided as are the distorted attempts that try to explain the results of modern scientific observation through misrepresented accounts of Genesis 1 that are viewed as scientifically binding.

With respect to the connections between the biblical accounts and science, the actual differences and challenges lie much deeper. They are evident in the basic passages of the first creation story, namely in the conviction that the creating will of God is fulfilled according to specific goals in the step-by-step formation of the forms of life on the earth, culminating in the creation of humanity.

This view of a goal-directed creation has again received a certain measure of support through the discovery of the so-called anthropic principle in modern cosmology; namely, that in the core of its development the cosmos must have already contained very precisely defined physical parameters so that structures like galaxies and systems of planets and the order of chemical elements that sustain life could develop from it.[43]

However, despite cosmology's connections to basic statements in the creation narrative, there remain the contradictions from evolutionary biology. Here it is not so much a question of the constancy of the life forms God created, or of the order of dinosaurs and other types of fossils, or even of the yet presumed "missing links." The decisive problem lies somewhere else: the creation story depicts a creation without suffering, in which the fact of death is not mentioned and in which the overabundance of plants can nourish the animals as well as the people. Such a world deserves God's judgment: see and it was very good!

According to science, however, a world like this has never existed. For the evolutionary biologist, the development of life forms is the result of a continual and terrible struggle for existence.

The leading branches of this process, which are directed by chance mutation and natural selection, constitute the "egoism of the gene." Indeed, it has led to continually adapting and life-sustaining forms of life, but also to many dead ends in evolution, which for most of today's biologists do not qualify as acceptable goals. The current position on evolution no longer presumes a gradual development from "lower" to "higher" forms of life that culminates in the creation of humans. One would have to regard this as entirely "external" to the stages of creation portrayed in Genesis 1. However, today's theory of evolution avoids any kind of judgment regarding "higher" and "lower," indicating that in the course of earth's history at least five stages can be defined through fossil identification. However, because of climate change and other catastrophes, the majority of these developed life forms died out.[44] In the evolution of life there is thus no recognizable "anthropological principle."[45]

The real question of biblical creation theology is not to what degree the observations of natural science see the origins of different forms of life as connected and what theory should be used to explain their development, but rather how the obvious reality of nature's fight for survival, which is also defined by suffering, can be reconciled with the claim of a creation characterized by a harmonious coexistence of all creatures.[46] At this point one would have to say that creation theology and science should then not be in competition with each other and would each be describing the reality created by God.

In his book *The World: Its Creation and Consummation*, Karl Heim writes that the biblical narrative of the six days of creation had "revealed the plan for creation in a retrospective prophesy."[47] He appears to have understood this in the sense that "an invisible hand" directed the pen of the priestly writer so that he could describe in detail the main features that, today, have been unearthed by paleontology. However, as we have seen, this is still a somewhat naive and apologist representation of the facts. However, one may ask whether the word of the "retrospective prophesy" does not have some deeper meaning. Was the biblical narrator interested in reporting about the actual reality of scientific research in his narrative of God's creation, or in describing God's created world was he less interested in the actual present world of the cosmos and more interested in the world that God intended? In this connection, Jürgen Ebach has described the first creation story as a "utopian recollection" since where it tells of the origin of human beings it also describes its own goal.[48] What does this mean for our understanding of the biblical account of God's creation?

We will have to pursue these questions further in the next section concerning the second creation story, specifically with respect to its account of paradise.

3. The Assignment and Humanity's Failure (2:4–3:24)

In Genesis 2:4, the story of God's creating activity appears to start afresh. Whereas 1:1 says, "In the beginning, God created the heavens and the earth," the section from 2:4b begins with, "When the LORD God made the earth and the heavens." That which in the first creation story was the goal of God's creation, namely, the creation of man, is pushed to the forefront of the second account. This is especially clear when we note that in the Hebrew text verses 5 and 6 are parenthetical remarks to the basic passage that states, "When the LORD God made the earth and the heavens . . . the LORD God formed the man from the dust of the ground." The creation of man thus becomes the center of the creating activity of God, focusing the perspective of the story of the cosmos on the story of humankind.

We have already briefly discussed the question of the order of 2:4a.[49] It was inserted during the editing of Genesis as a "subheading" and as a type of "bridge" between both of the first paragraphs: "This is the account of the heavens and the earth when they were created." The Hebrew word *toledot* that is used here and translated as "creation account" actually means "line" or "progeny" and is also used in 5:1, 10:1, 11:10, and so on to introduce the genealogies, particularly the story of the destiny of a family (compare 6:9). The "follow-up story" to the creation of heaven and earth is therefore the story of the creation of man and of his dominion over the earth.[50]

It is unmistakable that the new heading in 2:4b starts an entirely new narrative style. For almost a century there was a consensus among scholars that these verses marked the start of the oldest source of the Pentateuch, the so-called Jahwist. It got its name from the fact that in it the tetragraph JHWH is used from the beginning as the name for the God of Israel. It is regarded as very ancient and as dating back to the time of Solomon. However, as we have seen, in more recent times, a series of objections has been raised about this interpretation.[51] In particular, the existence of such an ancient, sole source for the Pentateuch has been placed in question—but not, however, because it comes before or continues on with the early history of the priestly writings, beginning with Genesis 1:1-3, 3 and continuing in Genesis 5 and in a string of narratives in 6–10, constituting a separate, independent story within the early history in Genesis 2:4b–11:9. It may have been inserted later together with a piece of the story containing the tradition of the original human parents and the events of the exodus on Sinai or worked independently into the narrative from the priestly writings. In any case, to date, there is no agreement on the chronology of the various layers in this process.[52]

Nevertheless, it is possible to leave this question open and to speak in a neutral way about the transmission of the early priestly writings. What is important for us is twofold: that we can observe the entire individual imprint of the context of the story that begins with Genesis 2:4b in the early biblical history *and* that we can trace the new connection that is evident throughout the entire texture of the early biblical story. The fact that the older account is placed next to the more recent one with its many universal statements gives it an overall framework out of which it may be read. In addition, the second story gains the character of a "recapitulation" of the creation story under different conditions, resulting in a change in perspective. The story of God's creation thus receives a new focus.

The Creation of Man

Man is now the focus of the story and the remainder of creation is his environment. The basic message of the first verses of this account, as we have seen, is that God at that time (i.e., in those days), when he made the earth and the heavens, also formed man and made him a living creature. Woven into this message is a kind of parenthetical declaration of what did not exist at the time: there were no shrubs or plants on the earth because God had not let it rain yet (!), and no humans existed to work the ground. These verses copy a convention of ancient oriental creation myths that often begin with the phrase "not yet."[53] The particular thing about this creation story is that nature (rain) and culture (working the ground) are seen from the very beginning as the preconditions for earth's ability to sustain life. Even if it hadn't yet rained, there was enough moisture (v. 6 in the unified translation) for God to form man from the earth (v. 7).

From the point of view of language, the Hebrew text already gives indications of the basic motif for the story, starting with verse 5, as well as the perspective that gave rise to it: the interdependency of the acre of earth (*'adamah*) and of man (*'adam*). At the same time, it points out that Adam is not a unique name but is the description of man as a type. The individual person is the *ben-'adam*, the son of man (compare Ps. 8:5: "What is man that you are mindful of him, the son of man that you care for him?").

This man is totally and completely an "earthly" creature, formed from the moist dust of the ground. His body is comprised of elements that are readily available in the earth. While it is clearly evident that the "dust" is stressed, the inner and external biblical image prevails that God formed man like a pot made from clay.[54] Obviously, the dispensability of man who "returns to dust" (compare 3:19) is also highlighted here.[55]

God gives life to this figure by breathing life into him. This is not a divine spark that is loaned out to man and it is not God's spirit or even—as is often supposed—some eternal (immortal) soul; rather, it is the life of the human body, the interconnectedness of the powers that lie in him that make him vastly more than the sum of the parts of "dust." The verse that follows underscores this: "And the man became a living being." Here also, as in 1:20, we find the Hebrew word *nephesh*, which is traditionally translated as "soul" and has thus led to the misunderstanding that man received an "immortal" soul through God's breath. However, the Hebrew text clearly indicates, "And man became a living soul." Accordingly, it does not mean just a part of man but rather the entirety of man in his whole lived existence. Also, the second creation account includes animals as "living creatures," just as the first one does (2:19, unified translation). Even according to Psalm 104:29 all living creatures are dependent on God's life-giving breath.

The Garden of Eden

In order to give man a place to live, God arranges for a garden in the east: in the direction of the setting sun is the location of awakening life. The landscape of Eden cannot be identified geographically; the Hebrew translates "Eden" as "delight" and thus in 2:15 and 3:23 (compare Isa. 51:3; Ezek. 28:13; 31:9, 16, 18; 36:35) Eden is the name given to the garden itself. The Septuagint, the Greek translation of the Old Testament, translates the word *garden* in 2:8 as *paradeisos* (from the Persian: "fenced-in garden of pleasure") and thus offers the term for the idea of "paradise," which is used in an eschatological sense in both the Jewish tradition and the New Testament (compare Ezek. 36:35; then test Lev. 18; 4 Ezra 7:123; Rev. 2:7; Luke 23:42; 2 Cor. 12:2-4).

The Garden of Eden in Genesis 2:8 is, however, located on earth. It is the epitome of earth as an environment for humans—a habitat that shows that what lies hidden in the earth is capable of bearing fruit. God does not invest in a special culture but allows all trees to grow on the earth. Their fruit helps sustain life and at the same time carries the fullness of life and joy of life for the existence of humankind. The fact that this fruit appears "seductive" and "luscious" does not have a negative connotation; God also gives the zest for life in the gifts of nature. With the "tree of the knowledge of good and evil" and the "tree of life" we have introduced, in symbolic form, the potential of the habitat of creation that is to be used by humans to bring them to the frontiers of their existence.

Nevertheless, this is not discussed at the start, and an unusual digression is contained in verses 10-14. In Eden, a great stream of water flows forth to water the garden and then separates into four parts, each of which continue to flow through the earth. The third and fourth of these are the Tigris and the Euphrates; both rivers flow through Mesopotamia and make it habitable. The rivers Pishon and Gihon are not identifiable, but the geographical location would seem to indicate Arabia (Havilah) and Nubia (Cush). The latter could have some connection to the Nile, but apparently here the symbolic (Pishon and Gihon) and the geographical (Euphrates and Tigris), and the four branches of the river of paradise, represent the life-giving water that comes from God's creating and nourishing activity in the entire world (the number four is used to describe the entire world). As a final indication of hope, the image is found again in Ezekiel 47:1-3, where a life-giving stream flows from the temple (compare Zech. 14:8 and Rev. 22).

Man's Purpose

Verse 15 once again picks up the threads of the story from verse 8: God takes man and places him in the Garden of Eden "to work it and take care of it."

The Garden of Eden is not a la-la land. Human work is seen as a part of the creating activity of God (compare v. 5). Man is not a cocreator, but a coworker with God who contributes to the "working and caretaking" of God's creative work. The "culture" of cultivating the earth and processing its gifts, and the "nature" of creation, which is worthy of care, belongs to the creating work that God had in mind for man.

As in the priestly version of the creation story, in the second account it is noticeable that there is not any connection to direct "service" to God, such as sacrifice of the fruits of the earth. The earth remains entirely for man, albeit clearly within the framework of the assignment God gives him.

The Forbidden Tree

The weaving together of the gift of freedom and of limitation is clearly portrayed in verse 16: "You are free to eat of any tree," God tells man and refers to the fullness and richness of creation that stands ready at man's disposal. But then the limit is declared: "You must not eat from the tree of the knowledge of good and evil."

What does "knowledge of good and evil" mean and why is there the prohibition not to eat from the fruit that gives knowledge? This motif has no parallel in biblical or ancient oriental literature to help explain. Using a rather simplistic outline, there are three possibilities.

(1) To know good and evil and to be able to decide between these two alternatives is a sign of maturity. Deuteronomy 1:39 talks about little children who "do not understand good or evil" and Isaiah 7:15 speaks of the ability "to reject the wrong and to choose the right" as a sign of maturity. Should God's command to man be

seen as a part of some kind of miserable adolescence and the dis-
obeying of the command as a step to more mature and seasoned
humanity? The biblical story does not see it this way; but this question has occupied many of today's interpreters, especially those
who take a philosophical perspective.

(2) By contrast, many modern interpreters think that the juxtaposition of "good and evil" in the language of the Bible does
not imply the "good and evil" of morality, but rather good and
bad in the sense of useful and harmful. To know good and evil
means also to know oneself, namely, what is beneficial and what
is harmful for one's own life. Such knowledge is the expression of
self-determined autonomy: "I know best for myself what is good
for me!"[56]

(3) Good and evil is a formula that stands for "everything" (compare 2 Sam. 14:17 with 14:20, especially "neither good nor evil" in
the sense of "not" in 2 Sam. 13:33; further in Gen. 31:24-29). The
knowledge of good and evil also means "knowledge that encompasses and defines all of humanity,"[57] the time-bound and practical knowledge that includes, in addition to sexual knowledge, the
knowledge of life and death.

These three possibilities for meaning are not sharply distinguished.[58] Most modern interpreters prefer the second option, but
that does not mean that they exclude the ideas of the others. All
basically describe positive goals. They are problematic when they
go beyond the authority of God, since then the striving for "good
and evil" becomes a means of securing for humankind some kind
of autonomous mastery of existence. Thus, the threatening sanction "for when you eat of it you will surely die" is not only an
external punishment of the law but an inner consequence of the
overstepping of limits set for man. It is therefore an open question
as to whether humans were originally intended to be immortal: it
is still not settled. In any case, death does not yet appear in God's
intended horizon of life.

A second question is therefore almost answered: why is the tree
of life not mentioned here? A simple explanation for this, and one
that many interpreters give, consists in the presumption that the
motif of the "tree of life" (which indeed has many parallels in the
biblical tradition and in those external to the Bible) was later
recorded as part of the story. That may be so, but the fact that one

simply may have forgotten to include the motif here would be too simple a solution. The "tree of life" and the "tree of the knowledge of good and evil" basically represent "two narrative accounts of the same tree constellation."[59] In any case, there is a delimiting line that people should beware of when seeking autonomous knowledge and trying to put themselves in God's place. (The snake in 3:5 is a thoroughly competent interpreter of this command!) Only when the limits are overstepped does the reality of death emerge on the scene of man's reality. And at that point the question of the meaning of "knowledge of good and evil" will be asked again.

A Helpful Partner

The narrative then takes another direction. It is related that the man receives a partner, or better stated, he is "adapted" to take on the fellowship of a partner. God says: "It is not good for the man to be alone. I will make a helper suitable for him." Man is a social creature. He needs community and assistance. Luther's translation of "a helpmate" has led to patriarchal thinking that is really quite foreign to this text. Rather, this help is thought of in terms of a competent partnership or as a "counterpart" (many translate this as "who corresponds to him").

It illustrates a story line that offers some very humorous anecdotes. God appears to be experimenting. Just as he made man from the earth, he also made the animals of the field and the birds of the air, to which man has a particular relationship. They are also "living beings" just like man is, and thus this creation story tells of the close relationship between animals and man. They are made from the same "stuff"—an idea that appears to be very modern if, in the place of the dust of the earth, one thinks in terms of the broader correspondence of the structure of DNA, particularly between vertebrates and man!

However—and here we have a very anthropocentric view of the animal world—animals are seen in relationship to man; he has the "power of definition." He assigns names and accordingly determines the nature of the animals. And although here an intensive relationship between man and animals is formed, the helper, the counterpart for man, is not found among the animals. Animals can be very close to man (and perhaps one could here write a small theology of a dog or a horse!), but they are essentially separate, which gives them their entirely independent value.

In order to prepare a partner for man, the Creator must go back to man himself: he causes him to fall into a deep sleep, takes a piece out of him (portrayed as a rib), "builds" a woman out of it, and brings it to the awakened man. Man is overcome: "This is now bone of my bones and flesh of my flesh!" And he also gives this new creature a name, which redefines his own existence. The play on words that lies at the basis in the Hebrew text is conveyed best in English: "This one shall be called woman (*issa*), for out of man (*is*) this one was taken."

Both the unity and difference of human existence are expressed through the difference in gender. The story does not give any indication as to whether it relies on an original myth of an androgynous early man out of which man and woman both originate, a motif that is often found in stories about the origin of man. Rather, the naming of the rib indicates that this idea should be rejected. However, it is clear that Adam is clearly "man" in contrast to "woman." The unity in body ("bone of my bones and flesh of my flesh") is the basis for the close affinity in the bond of partnership.

This affinity is emphasized through two basic observations. The first is formulated as a statement that is always the case regarding the intensity of the relationship between man and woman: "For this reason a man will leave his father and mother and be united to his wife." This is an unusual statement and seems to suggest a general state of affairs in human society. However, according to our knowledge, neither in Israel nor in the Orient was there a form of society in which a man left his family in order to be united with his wife. Othmar Keel and Silvia Schroer have suggested that *'azab* not only means "leave" but also "neglect" (compare Neh. 13:11). It has to do with "detachment" from parents.[60] Verse 24 describes the social reality not with institutional but with interpersonal concepts, which doubtless also apply for the continuation of this verse: "And they will become one flesh." Obviously, the sexual connection between man and woman is central to this statement, but not limited to it, as it describes the entire relationship between them both as well as their interdependence on each other. Almost all current interpretations point to the fact that the text does not form the basis for monogamous marriage. That may be correct. However, at the same time, in terms of the ancient world, it portrays in a very unique way the intimate relationship of a male and female pair as forming the core of human society. The fact that the Jesus tradition has used it to advance the indissolubility of marriage in the sense that men and women are to be continually responsible to each other (compare Mark 10:8; Matt. 19:5) is the result of this verse.

It is also significant that interpreters refer to the fact that, in the best sense of the word, this community is a "self-goal": the "being there for each other" of man and woman makes their humanity whole, although the aspect of procreation has yet to be mentioned.

The second claim that is made by this verse is valid only for the original state of man and woman: Adam and his wife were naked and were not ashamed. In the Old Testament, "to be naked" has less of a sexual connotation; rather, it is the expression of complete abandonment. Accordingly, the "shamelessness" of the first human pair is not so much an expression of sexual impartiality but the consequence of an early trust. The following section will go into this further.

Temptation and Failure

In chapter 3, a new story line begins with a new theme, but it is directly connected to the previous one. Many interpreters are of the opinion that in Genesis 2 and 3 two original and independent stories are combined together.[61] However, the end result is so seamless that it appears to be a connected whole (see Table 2). It is therefore important—and this is the consensus of modern interpreters—that chapter 2 does not represent an "original situation" in the sense of the condition of human existence as it developed after the Fall. Chapter 2 describes human existence as God wanted it to be, but chapter 3 describes how it has developed in actuality as the result of the sins of man and woman. Nevertheless, both aspects shed light on an important dimension of human existence.

Let us now return to the story of the temptation of man and woman and the breaking of God's commandment. In unique language and depth, the story portrays, step-by-step, how man and woman become corrupt. For observant readers it is clear: here in a very colorful and vivid way the basic events of human existence are told. Questions about the *how* and *when* of these events are really not essential. To ask, "How could the snake talk?" "How did God talk to man or make him clothes out of leaves?" can indeed be helpful for a certain level of realism but are still inadequate. It is quite clear that here, in the form of a story, basic statements are made about truth and the reality of human existence concerning the early beginnings of human life. Accordingly, the story actually needs almost no additional explanation. However, here are several clarifications:

In verse 1, with no other intermediary present, the snake is introduced as the voice of temptation. How does it get this role? The snake is arguably cleverer than all the other animals, something that can be seen as positive in the biblical tradition (compare Matt. 10:16). However, this positive aspect also contains a negative one and turns into the voice of temptation. In the created world there is always the potential for wickedness. One of the basic puzzles of the world, *Unde malum*? Where does evil come from? is suggested here, but not in a dualistic sense with any reference to an evil power external to God lying outside of the act of creation. The snake is not identified with Satan; it is an animal and one of God's "living creatures." But it is also a paradigm for the cleverness lying within God's creation that can be misused to challenge God. For, in addition to the basic trust imbued in God's creation, there is also mistrust as a result of the opposition between Creator and creation. His mouthpiece is thus the snake. Later on, in the temptation of Jesus in the wilderness, Satan again takes on this function by twisting God's words.

This is also the approach used in the snake's argument: Did God speak? Did he really mean what he said? What follows is a highly interesting psychological game of question and answer. The snake asks: "Did God really say, 'You must not eat from any tree in the garden'?" The generalization of the question leads to a misrepresentation and thus to a comparable overreaction by the woman. First, she says correctly, "We may eat fruit from the trees in the garden, but not from the tree that is in the middle of the garden." However, she then changes the words of God's command in defense against the temptation: "You shall not eat of it" appears as "You shall not touch it." Psychologically this is an overcompensation for the taboo, an expression of anxiety in view of the temptation, while at the same time unknowingly stressing its attraction.

The snake continues to probe using a series of half-truths. "You will not die," it says, and appears to have been proved right, since the person does not fall down dead after enjoying the forbidden fruit. But in the breaking of God's commandment and in the "knowledge of good and evil," the fate of death essentially does come upon them.

The snake goes on to say: "God knows that when you eat of it your eyes will be opened, and you will be like God, knowing good and evil." This lure hides a double probe: God would like to hold something back that should also be available to humans; and humans would be like God if they were to eat of the fruit that gives the knowledge of good and evil.

One thing is correct: humans can penetrate into the area of knowledge that God appears to withhold. The problem is, however, that man and woman cannot bear knowing this. They will never be like God, but in revolt against God they destroy their relationship to him. Finally, it has to do with a basic yearning at humanity's core. God has placed humans in relationship to him and given them the ability to know him. (The first creation story describes this fact using the motif of humans being made in God's image). This gives humans the ability to look beyond the edge of their existence and to overstep the perceived possibilities given by this ability. Thus, the knowledge of "good and evil" is a positive expression for the coming of age and the maturity of human existence.[62] However, man and woman cannot maintain the beneficial limit for their life that God has given in his commandment and have to overstep it. God's good intention is questioned; it is then perceived as injustice in order to justify the transgressing of the limit.

Verse 6 describes the essence of temptation in colorful words: "The woman saw that the fruit of the tree was good for food and pleasing to the eye, and also desirable for gaining wisdom." All of the senses are included and the suggestion that the forbidden fruit is the sweetest is very well depicted. However, at the same time there is something deeply tragic here: the gift of the Creator that humans should broaden their environment and have the joy of more knowledge and understanding leads to conflict with the

Creator. In a brief passage it then tells how the woman eats of the fruit and invites the man to be part of the temptation with her.

Verse 7 shows the consequences. The prediction of the snake is fulfilled, but with different results. Their eyes are opened and they know that they are naked. The knowledge of "good and evil" begins with the fact that they know that they see themselves. They recognize their sexual differences and with it their limitations; they know actual nakedness and cannot tolerate it. Broken trust with God destroys their innocent openness to the other. External nakedness is a sign for the inner vulnerability; sexual shame is a symptom of a deeper shame that can only be covered in a meager way by a fig leaf.

In the Eyes of God

In verse 8 what was once a trusting relationship with God now becomes a game of hide-and-seek that goes awry. Because man was entrusted with "good and evil," he must now hide from God. He is not only ashamed before God; he is also afraid of him. Fear is embedded in the life of the man who knows too much; he is aware of his own guilt and reckons it will not be without consequences. When God asks, "Adam, where are you?" it also marks the beginning of the story of God with humanity in which God continually searches man out in order to confront him with his deeds and their consequences and then, through the law, presents new possibilities for life.

At first, there is the typical example of trying to pass off the guilt: "The woman you put here with me—she gave me some fruit from the tree, and I ate it," says Adam (v. 12), and also implicates God as responsible for it. "The serpent deceived me, and I ate," says the woman (v. 13) as she pleads for milder treatment.

The serpent is not questioned because it is not responsible to the same degree as the man, and thus the question of the origin of evil remains open. The serpent does not represent an evil power but more closely embodies the potential for temptation that lies everywhere in the abundance of creation. To that extent the serpent is also affected by the consequences of the event.

God does not accept the strategy of excuses; rather, he requires everyone to take responsibility for what they have done.

Accordingly, man (in concrete terms Eve) is asked: "What is this you have done?" Evil emerged in the world through the breaking of God's commandment, or expressed in theological terms, which Genesis 3 still circumvents, sin emerges from the transgression.

The Consequences of Transgression

Quite possibly, in the original version, the banishment from the Garden of Eden was the immediate consequence of breaking God's command.[63] However, it was "broadened" very early on by the "curse" in verses 14-19. The disruption in the relationship of human beings to one another and to their environment is the result of transgressing the law and of a broken trust.

Accordingly, the curses that follow are not randomly assigned punishments but comprise the "curse of the bad deed." They do not address people directly. Humankind is not cursed, but the snake and the earth are cursed, and as a result the living conditions of humans are changed for the worse. In terms of content, the curse on the snake and the earth, and the consequences that are announced, have an etiological character—that is, they declare disaster as the consequence of the break in the relationship between God and humans. They do not represent God's will but are an "original fate" that burdens human beings because God requires humans to face the consequences of striving for the knowledge of good and evil. "The appropriate connections of creation in nature go awry. Animals become threatening and man's connection to work becomes drudgery; giving birth is painful and a balanced society of the sexes is replaced by one of dominance."[64]

In verses 14 and 15, the snake that had promised life and likeness to God must now crawl on the ground and eat dirt. From the embodiment of the enticing richness of creation it becomes a symbol of the earth's arrested existence and a representative of enmity between humans and animals. As a result of the snake and its descendants, humans experience something of the threat of death that hides in the animal world. Instead of being God, human beings are now in a permanent fight for survival from death and are consigned to the constant threat of death.

In verse 16 women's God-given honor and task of bringing children into the world is now connected with pain and danger. Thus, the relationship between man and woman is also distorted through the damage of a basic sense of trust: the woman is dependent in a new way and man will use this as a reason to dominate her. However, this dominance is different from what the Luther translation communicates, as God intends no hierarchy here ("He shall rule over you"); rather, it is the description of an equally weighted partnership ("He will rule over you").

Verse 17 gives a parallel to this in the complication of work for man. The alienation that characterizes the partnership also corresponds to the alienation of work. As a result, the cocreating job of working and protecting (the earth) now becomes a fight for survival.

And now death suddenly comes into view—not as a new fact or dramatic climax of divine punishment, but rather as the natural end to human life that also puts an end to the energy to fight for survival. Once more it is emphasized that man comes from the earth, but this time the particular transient and obsolete nature of human existence is stressed: "From dust you are and to dust you will return" (v. 19b). Instead of a retreat back to God, who has given man his life's breath, death is now a return to dust—a fate that naturally not just Adam as a man, but also the woman, must meet.

Provisions and Banishment

Verses 20 and 21 tell of two things that sound very surprising in light of the burdening of life expressed in the words of the curse. Adam gives his wife a name. One should have already expected this in 2:23. Her name also has general meaning, as does the name Adam. The woman's name is Eve (actually Chawwa), and with it the narrator conveys the word *life*. The foundation for the name, says Adam, is: "She would become the mother of all the living." This is essentially a phrase that would be better placed after the first birth, but here it is programmatic. Adam understands that even under divine law human life has a future. The story of humankind does not end until it begins correctly—through the immanent death of the first human couple. And even in light of death God sends new life: Eve will bear children and will become the mother of the human race.

In parallel to the second verse, God makes both Adam and his wife clothes from skins and dresses them. This is perhaps the most boldly anthropomorphic verse in the entire Bible! Like a furrier, God makes clothing for man and woman (where he got the pelts is not mentioned in the story) in order to give them the protection they need in place of the impractical leaves.

This does not, however, prevent the fact that now in verses 22-24 a very decisive consequence emerges as a result of the first human pair's transgression. God asserts that, in a certain respect, man has "become like one of us" (the plural is again the "plural of counsel," but could also include the "Elohim" as the divine). Since man knows what "good and evil" is, and because he knows what is beneficial and what is bad for him (even if he does not heed this knowledge), he therefore also knows the limits of death. His life has become "Being-unto-Death."[65] And here is also the danger that the man will eat from the tree of life and become immortal. That should not happen, but the narrator does not say why. He suggests that his readers already know how disastrous it would be for humankind if man were to also overstep these limits and, even if it seems worth striving for, "to live forever."

Although man is banished from the Garden of Eden, God's assignment for him is nevertheless renewed: he shall work the earth from which he came and to which he belongs! Responsibility for the earth remains, even outside of paradise! Cherubim, guardians of the divine world—who one imagines as lion-headed sphinxes with wings—and a flaming sword guard and block the way back into paradise and the tree of life.

Humans still find themselves in the conditions that are described in 3:14-19—in lives full of cares and worries, of envy and suffering, of striving for survival and defined by death. As we saw, the story of paradise was not intended to tell of a "golden age" of the beginning epoch of humanity. It tells of an unblemished life in unbroken community with God as the original perspective for human life with God, which was never realized but nevertheless should never be forgotten. The reality of existence after the break with God must be seen in all of its starkness. However, at the same time it should also be made clear that it does not depict the original creative will of God, thus harboring the question of its own legitimate obsolescence.

O. H. Steck has tried to describe the intention of the narrator in the portrayal of this tension:

> Thus, the Jahwist does not seek from among his readers people who long for the lost paradise and regret the current state and condition of man, but people of action who, in view of lost paradise and their fatal situation and their condition in all of its brokenness, still have an obvious trust in God's protection and blessing for human existence, which assumes in Genesis 12 a new behavior towards human existence thus creating the space for the actual advancement of human community through Yahweh in which the existence of any individual person will also be blessed.[66]

4. Creation, Sin, and Death—Further Questions Regarding Genesis 2 and 3

The arguments of current scholarship as well as the perspective of having been embedded into ancient oriental religious history and into the internal biblical tradition clearly differentiate the context of the early priestly writings from that of the priestly account of creation.

4.1 The Prehistory and Posthistory of the Story of Paradise

Although there are parallels in ancient oriental texts to individual motifs in the story (e.g., the motif of God's garden; the formation of man from clay; the symbol of the tree of life) in terms of the story as a whole, there are no immediate parallels existing outside of the biblical story.[67] The motif of forbidden fruit is often found in modern fairy tales (and also in other forms, such as a forbidden door, and so on), but not in ancient oriental myths.

The next parallel, which perhaps harks back to an early mythical stage of the story of early humankind, is found in Ezekiel 28:12-19 and is incorporated into the king of Tyre's lament for the dead (compare also Ezek. 31:15-18; Job 15:7).

The tradition of Adam and Eve and their disobedience is, apart from the original story, not mentioned once. The first Deutero-canonical, very short allusion to Adam and his dominance can be found in The Wisdom of Jesus Son of Sirach 49:16. At the same time, however, the apocalyptic literature begins with an intense preoccupation with Adam and the consequences of his disobedience. AthHen 32:6 mentions Adam and Eve briefly and their fate; Jubilees 3 retells Genesis 2:43–3:24, seeing in this account important clues to the instructions of Mosaic law. However, after the catastrophe of A.D. 70, the question of Adam's guilt and the disaster that he has brought upon humanity appears to be a more widespread theme in which the individual guilty entanglements are more thoroughly apparent: "Oh, Adam, what have you done? When you sinned, it didn't only affect you, but also your descendants. For what good is it to us if we are promised an immortal world when we have done a deed worthy of death?" (4 Ezra 7:118; similar is Syr. Bar. 48:42-47, where Eve is also mentioned, and 54:15).

The later version in the Apocalypse of Moses and its corollary Life of Adam and Eve treats the story of paradise quite extensively, and here the responsibility is very clearly assigned to Eve (Apoc. Mos. 21:6).

The Jewish philosopher Philo of Alexandria takes a very different direction. His interpretation of Genesis 1-3 asks about the nature of humans—primarily the nature of the relationship between spirit and humanity that defines human existence, which describes humans as being in the likeness of God—as well as the physical-psychic dimension that is discussed in Genesis 2 and 3.

The attempts of this platonic interpretation in the Hellenistic Jewish tradition are consequently radicalized through the *gnosis,* which strongly goes against the grain of the paradise story. Through the creation of Adam from the earth, the divine spirit is thus imprisoned in matter; the voice of the snake is then the voice of the true God who calls humans back to the freedom of divine existence. (In many interpretations Eve is even seen as the image of divine Sophia, who will lead Adam back on the correct path).[68]

Without a doubt, Paul's interpretation is the most influential for the Christian interpretation as well as for Western history. For him, Adam as the representative of sinful humanity is the counterpart to Christ as the representative of saved humanity. The verse from Romans 5:12 is central: "Therefore, just as sin entered the world through one man, and death through sin . . . in this way death came to all men, because all sinned" (compare the insertion of death from that in Gen. 3, where it is not talked about, with Wis. 2:24; Syr. Bar. 17:3; 23:4; 54:15; and also 1 Cor. 15:44)

What is thus decisive for Paul is that the rule of sin and death in humanity as defined by Adam is contrasted with the dominance of grace and life in humanity as defined by Christ (Rom. 5:18-23). In the example of Adam, Paul also mentions in Romans 7:7-13 the interconnection between law, temptation, transgression, sin, and death in the life of humanity.[69]

These verses, which have influenced all of Christian dogma, present us with a double challenge: how does the original intent of the paradise story relate to these verses and what do they mean for our knowledge today regarding the origin of *homo sapiens* and the close connection between life and death in nature?

4.2 The Philosophical and Psychological Interpretation of the Story of Paradise

If I am correct, Genesis 2 and 3 do not challenge the results of modern science in the same way that Genesis 1 does, even though the older story (Gen. 1) appears to be much stranger in terms of the evolutionary view of the origin of humans than does the later one (Gen. 2–3). Obviously, the anthropomorphic language in Genesis 2 and 3 has convinced both critics and defenders of the biblical text—perhaps with the exception of some very ingrained creationists—that these stories do not present something compatible with a scientific statement or report on the origins and early history of human beings but represent an essential description of human existence in the form of a story about God's creation and the first human couple, and of their guilty alienation from God.[70]

Thus, the early critical arguments with the text did not occur on the level of a small complaint of the type that showed God's activity, but with the criticism of the intended underlying basic statements. An example of this is Kant's observation at the end of his short work *The Presumed Beginning of Human History*:

> From this depiction of the early human history we have the exit, introduced through reason, of man from the first stage of his condition in paradise as nothing other than the crossing over from the crudeness of a mere animal creature into humanity, from

dependency on instinct to the guidance of reason, in short: from the tutelage of nature into the condition of freedom.[71]

Also, for Hegel the actual development of humanity first occurred with the decision to eat of the fruit of the tree of knowledge of good and evil. Clearly Hegel conceives of this event more dialectically than Kant does. In taking this action humans step from out of their unconscious innocence, allowing them to be found guilty, even though they follow their divine designation by doing it. "Whereas the animal being one with nature cannot be evil . . . man, in the act of knowledge, steps out of unity with nature, and this division itself, which is necessarily part of knowledge or sentience, makes us evil."[72]

In his book *The Concept of Anxiety*, Kierkegaard has critically discussed the dialectical postulate of the necessity of guilt for the process of humankind's development. For Kierkegaard it was important that even a psychological interpretation of the story of the Fall not hide the "qualitative leap" of guilt. In *The Concept of Anxiety*, he finds a definition of guilt that explains how guilt came to be, without making it a necessity.[73]

Kierkegaard concerns himself with the definition of the relationship between sin and sexuality, without agreeing to Augustine's link between concupiscence and sin: "Sinfulness is by no means sensuousness, but without sin there is no sexuality, and without sexuality, no history."[74]

It is no wonder that psychiatry and psychoanalysis have gravitated to this biblical text from among all others. The Freudian school primarily sees in the snake (and the tree) phallic symbols, and in the temptation of the snake the challenge of (forbidden) incestuous relations with the father.[75] The motif of forbidden fruit signals a regression from the genital level to the oral level; a symbol of the Oedipal sexual prohibition serves to "express of the general human experience of guilt."[76] However, the symbols can mean many things. The fruit refers also to the image of the motherly tree of life; and even the snake can be defined as the repressed divine mother, or as the voice of the *amina*, or even as the alter ego of Eve.[77]

A Jungian interpretation is also applicable here, where it sees in the snake an "archetype of life" in which the "physical not-I, the individual Other, Unliving, Beginning . . . Seductively Contradictory . . . Unconscious in contrast to the Conscious-I . . . the Inferior over against the differentiated function is expressed. . . . The voice of the snake invites the dark side of the soul in."[78] This leads to regression. However, the opportunity for regression also yields the unfolding of a richer life and a more responsive consciousness.

> The prohibition to not eat of the tree of knowledge means in this sense an act of self-insight, which leads an unleashing of the original unity into the unconscious. Thus, a higher, more vital existence is won in the tension between good and evil, consciousness and the unconscious, nature and culture; a benefit which more closely resembles the loss and pain that follows the loss of the original unity of paradise, since the lack of self-insight itself presents a much greater evil than does the bifurcation of a conscious life; accordingly, this is everyone's inevitable fate with respect to the demand to become conscious.[79]

The story of the Fall is thus for Jung "the psychologically necessary step to individuation, to self-consciousness, and brings with it the difference between good and evil, which the unconscious doesn't recognize."[80]

The observations of developmental psychologist Lieselotte Arnold-Carey point in a similar direction. In her therapeutic work with children she has determined that consciousness of guilt is connected on an "elementary level with the knowledge of the other gender . . . whose gender is not identical with that of the person knowing. In other words, a feeling of guilt occurs or is introduced when the identity is eliminated; it is not the result of repressive upbringing."[81]

Arnold-Carey ties these observations directly to the story of the Fall and writes: "Once more the act of knowledge, of being in the likeness of God, goes wrong in space and time. Not the being, but rather the doing, makes for the likeness." In one of the first summaries she writes: "Children have shown us that the apple of knowledge is a very bitter one when it brings duality as the bifurcation of consciousness. It is already bitter enough that it provokes knowledge of space and time and death, and guilt provokes and presents its own challenges."[82]

The process of discovering one's identity is thus a necessary step. However, it allows the person who wants to overstep his or her limits to also be aware of these limits and the specific dangers. Not to deny these limits, but also not to rebel against them or to take issue with them, is the lifelong task of humankind.

All of these interpretations have in common the fact that they essentially see in the forbidden fruit and the striving for knowledge of good and evil a necessary step to becoming human, especially for the acquisition of consciousness and for the individuation of human identity. Contrary to Kant, most of the later interpreters recognize that becoming guilty is unavoidable—and see in it a decisive step to maturation.

Quite possibly this interpretation is not as far removed from the original intention of the text as traditional Christian interpretation would want us to suppose. The Old Testament narrative contains a remarkable dialectic in making the connection between the motif of knowledge of good and evil and the prohibition to eat of the fruit of the tree of knowledge. Even for the narrator of Genesis 3 there is no doubt that "he sees in the wisdom a positive possibility for man, which man's existence enhances and which brings about accomplishments and successes. Still, these positive abilities of man for a rational form of existence from which the person can neither leave nor should . . . always lead to the person going awry in life; he fails as a creature, and he even goes against his Creator."[83] The actual problem that brings the tragedy into the realm of guilt is that the person wants to know and to define for himself or herself alone what is beneficial or harmful for his or her life, or good or bad, and thus puts himself or herself in God's place. Thus, in Genesis 3 "exactly the human striving for autonomous self-formation of one's own existence is conceived as the evil, which disrupts the existence and makeup of society."[84]

Here the interpretation of Horst Eberhard Richter in his book *The God Complex*, which does not actually give an interpretation of the Genesis text but presents a look into the history in which the experiences of the individual and the social effects are seen as interacting together in convincing ways, is helpful. Richter describes the disastrous path of modern humans who put themselves in God's place and as a result are threatened by ruin by replacing religion with some kind of other, yet powerful, functioning fantasy. In the story of the Fall what is said about the deathly consequences of temptation and the will to be like God is what Richter sees fulfilled in the personal and social crises of our time. What's more, he draws different consequences in his analysis; namely, not the affirmation of God but the "affirmation of death" is the "condition for the downfall of the God complex and the winning of a human measure between helplessness and almighty power."[85]

This calls for a decidedly theological interpretation of the story of creation and the Fall of humankind.

4.3 Sin and Death as Catastrophe

Adam—and, in her own way, Eve—are representatives of humankind. What is told about them are not stories of remarkable events from the early history of humanity, but what they experience marks the very essence of humanity and describes what humans are made of.

In connection with Genesis 3:23 and in reference to 4:16, one could say that human existence is life "this side of Eden." This has a double meaning. To human existence belongs the remembrance of the actuality of human life, which is not defined on the basis of the alienation of life. Human life encompasses the knowledge of the fullness of the possibilities of life, which God in his goodness has sent. Nonetheless, to human existence belongs a known or unknown knowledge that the hallmark of human existence also involves the collapse of heeding limitations. In it lies a deep tragedy but also a fatal primeval guilt, to the extent that the person loses his or her humanity precisely in the act of apparent maturity, namely, through the act of wanting to know for himself or herself what good and evil is. The biblical account does not speak of sin in this regard, but highlights a basic disturbance in the life of the person and his or her relationship to God. The fact that the Christian tradition has designated this continuing disturbance, at least in German-speaking areas, as "original sin" is extremely unfortunate. In the English language one speaks of original sin, just as the Latin denotes *peccatum originale*. In German, we speak of "prior sin." Prior sin describes a break in the relationship between God and ourselves, for a person is always caught in a prior condition of his or her own existence, which at the same time is validated by his or her own behavior.[86]

In this way, Paul's theme is employed. For him, Adam is representative of all of humanity, which includes Eve. With Paul we have, analogous to Jewish tradition, the woman Eve as the actual guilty one.[87] According to Romans 7:7-13, the paradise story is inescapably repeated anew in every person. Thus, Paul says in Romans 5:12 that these sins came into the world through one person, "because all have sinned." Accordingly, being a sinner—but also the need for salvation—is for all humans at all times both destiny and work.[88]

Although in Genesis 2 and 3 it appears that humans, like all God's creatures, were mortal from the beginning and that the Fall placed this reality in a new, more dismal perspective of a life distant from God, for Paul death is the consequence of the sin of the first man (Rom. 5:12). He therefore continues along the corresponding theological tradition of early Judaism.[89]

For Paul, the interpretation of universal sin and the sickness unto death of humanity is placed entirely in the service of soteriology. In general and without exception, humanity since Adam has been subject to the lordship of sin and of death so that in essence a new humanity begins with Christ under the lordship of grace, justification, and life (Rom. 5:18). Death is not a "punishment" God inflicts on humanity; it is rather the unavoidable consequence of separation from God as the source of life. "Death is the payment for sin"—that is, death is what "sin pays out . . . to its soldiers." Life, however, is God's gracious gift to those who are called into his service (Rom. 6:23).[90] It is not only people who suffer under decay and death; all of creation groans under its fate and hopes for the liberation of the children of God from the yoke of decay, since here also begins the salvation of the rest of creation (Rom. 8:18-22).

These verses do not merely stand in a certain tension to Old Testament interpretation (i.e., that decay and death belong to the essence of all creatures and also to humans, which clearly in both creation accounts is not mentioned at all or only in passing); they also stand in contrast to a basic knowledge of today's science. There are three areas that should be noted in particular.

1. The Origins of Humanity from the First Human Pair

Interestingly enough, here modern research has produced results that reveal a certain complement to the biblical account. The genetic analysis of various populations has found that today's existing *homo sapiens* can be traced back to a single origin. This theory has its detractors, but the majority of researchers still side with this conviction. One speaks of the "Eve of the mitochondria," a hypothetical original premother of the human race who is supposed to have lived not in Mesopotamia but in Africa.[91] Thus, a single individual is not necessarily postulated as the origin of humanity, but the heritage of all people is seen as stemming from the same ancestors; thus any ideology of separate races does not hold water. The unity of the human race and its biological and behavioral heritage has been impressively confirmed.

The first creation story does not fundamentally speak of the first human pair but of the collective *'adam* of humanity, from which male and female were created. The second, albeit older, narrative illustrates this in the style of an ancient oriental myth through the form of Adam and Eve. Even the Adam-Christ typology in Romans 5 does not force a historical analogy between the persons of Jesus and Adam. The typological parallels of both persons, which individually represent the old and the new humanity, do not, for Paul, exclude categorical differences.

2. The Boundary between Animal and Human Existence

Here the situation becomes murky. The first creation story appears to make a clear distinction in its portrayal of humans as being made in the image of God, a distinction that is made in Genesis 2 in the story of the creation of Eve for the sake of social relationships. Accordingly, Catholic dogma still sees an "ontological leap" between animals and humans, even today.[92] The biology of evolution, however, talks about an "animal-human continuum" in which, during the last century, ever new and intermediate steps between human-looking primates and early types of the genus of *homo* have been found. In terms of biological and anthropological research, various characteristics define humanity: walking upright, the largeness of the brain in relationship to the rest of the body, and the ability to use tools and language (for which the corresponding network of abilities regulated by the frontal cortex of the brain, as well as the ability to speak because of the position of the human voice box, are also determinative). To some extent, there were characteristics such as upright stance and use of tools that were already evidenced in the Australopithecines (counted as human). The size of the brain gradually increased in this line of development. Now, with the help of sign language, chimpanzees and baboons have even been able to learn basic elements of human communication. However, it is debated whether the Neanderthal may have exhibited the ability for language as we know it today.[93]

At what stage of development, then, should it be said that humans "become humans" according to the biblical account? We should remember that the biblical accounts do not see humans "biologically" as a separate category from animals. According to Genesis 2, God makes man and the animals from the same stuff—from the earth—and allows them to become "living beings" (vv. 7 and 19). In Genesis 1 it says that on the sixth day God "makes" the animals of the earth and humans (vv. 25 and 26), a statement that is very consciously juxtaposed right next to the celebratory account of his creating humans in his own image. The special nature of being human therefore does not lie in biological traits, but in man and woman's special relationship to God, which is expressed in their being conscious of God and thus also conscious of themselves.

From the point of view of many biologists, humankind's particular type of consciousness is a decisive hallmark of being human. This occurrence, however, cannot be determined by unearthing fossils, and also not just by virtue of the size of the brain. In any case, recent research suggests that the appearance of religious sensibilities or ties, as shown by certain use of tools, images, or figures, is also an important hallmark of human existence. Even if these legacies of *homo sapiens* cannot be factually confirmed from the very beginning of humankind's existence, nevertheless about thirty thousand years ago it is supposed that, in general, this dimension belonged to humankind, and there are even indications as to which evolutionary preference gave rise to human religious consciousness.[94] However, many researchers, such as the Australian neurophysiologist John Eccles, see in the origin of human consciousness a phenomenon that cannot be simply explained through the mechanism of evolution but can only be understood as a special type of divine creation.[95] There have been many salient arguments against this. However, there are also other researchers who convincingly say that even the human "spirit" is nothing other than a product of evolution's natural selection, and who see human beings as having a particular sensibility that is based in their developed consciousness.[96] Richard Leakey, who describes himself as in "no formal way religious," was asked whether he has known of a monkey that knew what sin was. He responded:

> I am very sure that monkeys and especially chimpanzees know in certain circumstances that many actions in social dealings are not appropriate. But monkeys are not burdened with the higher spiritual concept of sin. On the other hand, our forefathers from the earliest times carried this burden and, in my opinion, very well; it is the result of evolution in the difficult socially imprinted arena of human life.[97]

He views humanity's "powerful estimation of religion" in this way: "The striving for an explanation, whether it is expressed by religion, philosophy, or science, most certainly makes for a large divide between mankind and all other living creatures on today's earth."[98]

The biblical creation story only gives one reason for human striving for knowledge: God himself planted the question of God in the hearts of humans when he created humans in his image. And it is directly connected with the consciousness of responsibility for others and for God's creation. The biblical account does not give a reason for why humans waste both the question of God and the consciousness of responsibility, but it does make clear that the existential and social break in our present humanity, precisely because it is so deep and so painful, harks back to an original gift and definition of humanity given by God. It is not easy to tell this story from the very beginning in the language of today's science, and thus we must start at a point in time when the first representatives of the species *homo sapiens*, as they were intended by God, stepped onto the scene. However, we can also determine, in light of what has influenced humanity from the beginning, why we are human and what exactly the special gifts and callings of our humanity are, while still overlooking the fact that we are unlike any other living creature.

3. Death as Payment for Sin

Death came through sin into the world—so we read in Romans 5:12. Death came with *volvox* into the world—as I learned it in school. Our teachers taught us that the death of a single individual was the price of a differentiated collective and that this made organisms indeed more suited to life and adaptable but also robbed them of the possibility of prevailing through a continually new process of cell division.[99]

The limits of an individual organism's lifespan is also the pre-condition for the emergence of new individual forms of life and thus for the progress of evolution.[100] Thus, death is seen in terms of biology as the condition for emerging new life. The fact that, through the sin of the first human pair, death (as Rom. 8:20 appears to indicate) decay, and suffering of all living creatures came into the world contradicts all of the results of scientific research concerning the history of life on this planet. Even if death was not a condition of life at the start, it nevertheless became its early companion, and global catastrophes have continued to destroy large populations and entire forms of life.

We have already suggested that there are differences between the biblical accounts regarding these questions. Whereas the first creation story does not talk about death at all, it does appear in the second account and, despite a certain lack of clarity, is assumed to be a natural phenomenon of life. Mortality belongs to the earthly, created existence of humans just as it does to all other creatures (Gen. 3:19b).[101]

> But sin changes death: it gives it a kick that it otherwise would not have had. As long as sin reigns over man, it is connected with dying and death and the threat of *definitive failure*, ultimate waywardness. . . . However, thus the [creature] becomes something else; he experiences a "second" destructive death . . . that applies to him in a direct and actual sense: he is now nothing other than a consequence of sin.[102]

This is not articulated in Genesis 3, but is given a much more extensive and thoroughly correct interpretation by Paul.

The ability to recognize the break in one's own life also makes suffering palpable for the creature, and dying is seen not only as a natural "dying and becoming" but is experienced as an "anxious waiting" and "sighing" for salvation and liberation (Rom. 8:19-22). Although it is God's creation, the world as it is does not simply represent God's will. Whoever believes in God the Creator also hopes for salvation. This claim leads us once more to some very basic questions about the relationship between belief in creation and what human research says about the development and "functioning" of our world.

5. Creation or Nature—The Biblical Message and Modern Research

5.1 God as Creator, the World as Creation, and Humans as Creatures

I will first try to briefly summarize the passages in Genesis 1–3. Both accounts, as different as they are, place God's activity at the center. A simple linguistic analysis of the text makes clear to us that God is the acting subject in many of the passages, with the distinctive exception of 3:1-8. In Genesis 1, God's sovereign, unconditional, creating activity is entirely at the forefront, which clearly does not exclude the possibility that God's creating activity also means that those who are created are capable of bringing forth new creatures (compare 1:11, 24). Heaven and earth are formed as the realm of life and are to be occupied by the fullness of life in all of its different forms. Thus, creation corresponds to the being and the will of God.

At the same time, however, God remains the sovereign partner in his own creation, defining it through his "yes" and the predicate "very good" (compare 1:31). He does not dwell in it, but encloses and transcends it, which, among other things, is also expressed by the statement that God rested from his work on the seventh day. This partnership is maintained by the conscious monotheistic orientation of this narrative in contrast to the polytheistic myths of the time, which are "demythologized" because they represent—as Jan Assman has very impressively shown—a "cosmotheistic" understanding of the world. From this perspective, the powers that have called this world into existence and maintain it, but which also threaten it, are identified as divine entities. For the Bible, the world indeed has a divine origin because God created it; but that does not make it divine. Thus, it offers no images that represent God or to which one could pray as a surrogate for him. Rather, the passage stating that the person is made in the image of God has an entirely different function. The person is "in his freedom, independence, and responsibility . . . an image of God. . . . The person is to take charge of the world. Thus, he recognizes that it is not divine, and especially where the exclusive divinity of God's external world is concerned."[103] Thus, in the relationship of humans to God as the *one* God, who remains in partnership with his creation, the origin of freedom is founded in relationship to God but also includes the attempt at self-chosen autonomy in which the person recklessly uses his or her authority over creation for his or her own purposes. In order to better illustrate what happens when humanity's relationship with God malfunctions, and functioning as the climax of the story, the account in Genesis 2 and 3 clearly refers in its own way to humankind's value as well as to the task that is assigned to humankind.

The account in Genesis 1–3 is permeated with a basic tension. Both accounts want to make clear that God's creation is originally "very good" (1:31), especially when it describes the Garden of Eden as a nearly sacred world. At the same time, the early priestly account in Genesis 3 makes clear that humans find themselves from the beginning in a broken and encumbered existence that they themselves have caused. Banishment from the Garden of Eden is not a historical event but a basic element of human existence. As the context is now, this perspective also influences the passages in Genesis 1–3, and the continuation of the story shows that the priestly writings were aware from the start that their account of creation was not simply a photograph of the existing world.

However, the fact that both of the creation stories describe the origin of the world and the origin of humanity in such complete harmony leads to a conflict with today's view of science, which extends on a very fundamental level into many differences with the portrayal of the events as they were recorded as well as how they were expressed at the time.

5.2 Connections and Contradictions

When Napoleon Bonaparte asked Pierre-Simon Laplace why he did not mention God in his book on the mechanics of the heavens,

Laplace is said to have answered, "Sire, I managed without that hypothesis." This response appears to conclude that a competent scientific explanation of the origin of the world, of life, and of humanity can be arrived at without any mention of God's creating activity. And until far into the twentieth century, it was not only assumed and understood by many scientists that only "atheistic" methods were appropriate for their individual area of research, but they also pursued a completely atheistic explanation of the world as a whole.

It has been only since the last third of the last century, and primarily among the Anglo-Saxons, that serious discussions have emerged again between scientists and theologians in which, from the theological side, the claim has not only been made concerning the "that" of the creation of the world through God, but also serious consideration has been given to whether and in what way the "how" of scientific discovery has been capable of describing God's activity. It is primarily the results of modern physics and cosmology that have afforded the connecting points for a renewed and deeper discussion between science and theology.

Perhaps the most important impetus for a new consideration of the biblical account of creation is the knowledge that this universe did have a beginning (and quite possibly also an end). Many important scientists fought against this assumption for a long time because it was not compatible with their convictions about the eternal nature of matter. Pope Pius XII had already rejected the idea of the Big Bang as evidence of God's creation of the world.[104] Nevertheless, even Christian-oriented scientists warned against too quick an "exploitation" of the "standard model" for theological purposes.[105] The idea of the Big Bang—in scientific terms the assumption of a singular entity at the beginning of the origin of our universe—basically does not allow for anything that came "before" this moment. In addition, the element of time also emerges at the beginning—a fact that was already known to Augustine, who said that God had created time along with the world.[106]

The discovery of the "anthropological principle" has also provided the occasion for much discussion. It draws out the consequences from the observation that from the first moments of the origin of the world specific conditions regarding certain characteristics of matter—its rate of expansion, its isotopes, entropy, and spatial homogeneity—would have had to have existed (and actually do exist) so that this universe, our galaxy, the solar system, and finally life on earth could come into being.

In its "weak" form, the anthropological principle appears almost as a tautology when it says, "Because there are observers of this universe, the universe must have characteristics that allow for the existence of these observers." In contrast, the "strong" version says, "The universe, in its laws and in its particular makeup, must be thus created so that at some point in time it inevitably will be able to produce an observer."[107]

For many researchers the strong anthropological principle is not exactly proof of God, but it is still a convincing indication of the existence of a divine plan that one can deduce from the story of our universe. Others—even theologians—warn about making a retrospective connection from the results of cosmological development and superimposing a divine plan onto it.[108] The anthropological principle is also given special consideration in connection with quantum physics, which first observed a process in the quantum unit that moved it (i.e., the anthropological principle) from a potentiality to a reality. John D. Barrow and Frank J. Tipler thus formulate the "participatory anthropological principle," "Observers are necessarily brought into existence from the universe," and connect this with a teleological version of the principle. "There is a possible universe in which the goal is 'designed' to generate and maintain observers."[109] This appears less likely to correspond with the biblical faith in creation than with a cosmological variation of the Hegelian interpretation that says that through human knowledge of the world the "world spirit" first comes to know itself![110] However, even if one refrains from such speculative arguments, it is remarkable to note that in the anthropological principle scientific cosmology has finally been taken seriously, which up until now was only reserved for creationist thought.

A further intersecting point for dialogue lies with quantum physics' removal of the mechanistic cause-and-effect thinking for processes involving the atomic and subatomic realms. Here the question is interesting as to whether the creative and the creating action of God is conceivable within a nondeterministic ontology— namely, "that God engages directly in the physical world without breaking physical laws and determines (otherwise undefined) quantum events."[111]

In parallel, the chaos theory demonstrates using examples of so-called more open and particular dissipative systems that in the macroarea are processes, which, despite the remaining validity of causal laws, do not proceed in a determinative fashion but nonetheless reveal a certain order. Thus, there is the related conviction that behind this order God is seen as the "great attractor," a concept that is used in the theory of chaos to describe a large entity that cannot be predicted from individual events.[112]

All these connecting points of reference stem from the area of physics, especially that of cosmology. In biology, similar phenomena appear to be lacking. Indeed, today's concept of evolution and the development of the universe includes the unfolding of life in all of its biological manifestations. Although cosmological developments appear to come straight from the first beginnings of the origin of the galaxies and the "life phases" of certain stars, continuing on to the emergence of the solar system and of planet earth, biological evolution is not as "goal directed." There are clearly no biological "anthropic principles" and no "tree of origin" in evolution suggesting that humankind is the crowning point, but rather there is a broadly branching "bush landscape" with many forms of life, originating partially from natural or even catastrophic forces. Humankind is one—but not by any means the only—relatively successful species in this game of trial and error. Thus, it is today's biologists who, as missionaries of an ideological atheism, support and defend the view of senseless suffering that is tied to the theory of evolution.[113] However, there are other biologists who refute this. Kenneth R. Miller writes in his book *Finding Darwin's God:* "Neither the self-sufficiency of nature nor the reality of evil in the world mean God is absent. To a religious person, both signify something quite different—the strength of God's love and the reality of our freedom as His creatures." And he defends this on the basis of clear affirmation of evolutionary teaching: "To people of faith, what evolution says is that nature is complete. God fashioned a material world in which truly free, truly independent beings could evolve. He got it right the very first time."[114]

Which position is right? Does the biblical account of creation harmonize at all with the scientific explanation of the origin of life with its array of species, according to the model of evolution, or at least relate to it in some way?

5.3 Scientific Theory and God's Creating Activity

The question of how the biblical account of God's creating activity and the results and models of the conclusions of scientific research can be brought into a fruitful dialogue with each other has produced a wealth of literature over the last twenty-five to thirty years, something that should not be overlooked anymore. Many scientists write popular books that end with a religious or theological question.[115] There are also a variety of conferences and symposia yielding representation from very different subjects. Most of them, however, are not able to form a synthesis,[116] and yet there are many authors with scientific and theological training who attempt to develop these syntheses.[117]

In accord with Sigurd Daecke, the various results can be summarized under three main headings.[118]

1. Creation or Evolution

This is the position over which even inveterate creationists are divided, similar to the declared opponents of any religious interpretation—but under the opposite sign. For authors such as Amos Wilder-Smith or Werner Gitt, any deviation from the statements of biblical creation accounts and any inclusion of statements from the model of evolution, as in the sense of a "theistic evolution," are a betrayal of the Christian faith.[119] On the opposite side, biologists like Jacques Monod, Richard Dawkins, Edward O. Wilson, or Franz M. Wuketits do not allow any room for the idea of divine activity in the origin of the universe or in the origin of life and its development on earth. The fact of evolution, as they see it, also does not allow for any questions about the meaning of this world and the life in it. Steven Hawking also appears to be of the view that an explanation for our entire universe and its origins allows no room for a Creator.[120]

However, it should be emphasized that not all those who place the biblical conception of creation in the context of scientific statements according to the model of evolution think this way. There are also creationist-minded scholars who do not exclude the subarea of the idea of evolution, just as there are scientists who see in the theory of evolution no adequate explanation of the origin of life and its many forms yet still do not consider themselves creationists.[121] This leads us to the second position.

2. Creation and Evolution

This is quite possibly the classic position of twentieth-century theology. The concept of "creation" belongs in the area of theology, and evolution belongs in the area of science. Both describe various dimensions of our reality, but do not appear to be in competition with each other.

In his foreword to his lectures on creation (*Church Dogmatics* III/1), Karl Barth wrote impressively how it had become clear to him that

> in view of what the Holy Scriptures and the Christian church understands under God's creating activity, there can be absolutely no scientific questions, objections, or even helpful solutions. . . . For science has free scope on the side of what theology describes as the work of the Creator. And theology may and must remain free, whereas science, which is only science and not secretly a heathen gnosis or religion, has its own limitations.

He also emphasizes that "future workers in the field of the Christian doctrine of creation will find many problems worth pondering in defining the point and manner of this twofold boundary." A corresponding position by Karl Rahner is also often cited: "Theology and science do not basically contradict each other, because both are from the beginning different in their respective areas and their methods."[122]

As for the scientists, there is often the appeal for a clean separation between the areas concerned, as is the case with Max Planck or Werner Heisenberg and many others.[123] In view of the broadening speculation by modern natural philosophy in the second half of the twentieth century, the theologian and physicist Hans-Dieter Mutschler has recently warned against blurring the boundaries between physics and religion.[124]

However, over the last thirty years, the lack of a relationship between the claims of faith and scientific knowledge was perceived as unsatisfactory, since both ultimately still wanted to speak for the same actuality.

The simplest relationship between these areas is an additive: creation is the nondeducible beginning event of a singular origin of the universe that is scientifically unexplainable in which are embedded the already essential hallmarks of future development. Evolution, however, is the event of the *creatio continua* in which the development of the cosmos and the formation of different forms of life unfold in a certain kind of freedom but still along the basic lines of the original creative impulse. The image of the Creator is thus no longer that of the watchmaker who assembles the great world clock that then mechanistically, and without any further handling, runs forever according to predetermined laws. Rather, God created a completely self-contained, organized system that is "pro-grammed" according to an intelligent plan ("intelligent design") so that it unfolds according to his will in the interplay between rules and chance.[125] But with this we are almost at the third position.

3. Creation as Evolution

Here the juxtaposition of creation and evolution results in an integrative relationship between both. In the event of evolution God creates the world. This is a conviction shared by many of today's theologians and scientists. However, what does this mean for our understanding of God? Does that mean, as Erich Jantsch argues, that God is not an absolute, but "he himself evolves—he *is* evolution"?[126]

Such ideas are clearly rooted theologically in mysticism or in Buddhism, but are also expressed in the process theology of Alfred North Whitehead and were further developed by a series of theologians into a process theology—significant for a doctrine of creation that takes into consideration the challenges of science.[127]

God is the "source of order" as well as the "source of the new," making possible the self-creating impulse of the individual being, and "in this way makes freedom possible, as well as structure and justice."[128] He is, however, also influenced by the events of the world and is "the great guardian—the companion of suffering, who understands."[129] "God's love is the deepest sympathetic par-ticipation in the process of the world's events."[130] Thus, this is also a certain answer to the question of theodicy. God suffers with the sufferings of the world, and it is the cross of Christ that reveals this side of divine reality.

Despite its closeness to biblical theology, there are several objections regarding the appropriateness of process theology. Its dynamic interweaving of God's action and the developments of nature and life approaches pantheism. Whitehead also says: "It is as true to say that God created the world as it is to claim that the world created God."[131] This, however, contradicts biblical passages on creation.

As a result, John Polkinghorne argues for a revised form of theism in which God's sovereign creating activity is tied with an openness to the development of the world in time,[132] whereas Arthur Peacocke finds in pantheism an expression of God's transcendence as well as his immanence and that God's partnership with creation and his immanence in it are both maintained.[133]

Despite all of these objections, the view of the ongoing creating activity of God, namely the *creatio continua*, is at the forefront. The fact that God creates a self-contained, organized system, which he then leaves to itself, does not correspond to passages in biblical accounts of creation, even where creation is mentioned from the very start. God accompanies what he has created in ongoing creating activity.

However, the way in which God works in creating and directing the events of the world without placing this claim in competition with scientifically established causality, thus making God into a "physical interventionist," is described in various ways. Many theologians formally distinguish between God as the "primary cause" and God as the "secondary cause," as science would describe it.[134] Others seek more precise explanations. Polkinghorne speaks of a "continuing abundance of information" coming from God according to the model of an open system of chaos.[135] Peacocke describes God's activity as the effect of a "downward-leading causality [focused] on the world."[136] Wolfhart Pannenberg compares God's activity in nature to the workings of an electromagnetic field.[137] Others place God's action in the microrealm of quantum processes.[138] However, the entire line of questioning is misguided because, as Daecke suggests, it sees "creation as *interpretation* of evolution and evolution as the *concretizing* of creation" and views God's creating activity as having an immanent effect in the evolutionary process.[139]

5.4 The Consistent Message of Biblical Faith in Creation

As impressive as the attempt is to bring Christian faith in creation into agreement with the scientific theory of nature, it is still clear that a complete synchronization would be quite problematic. The attempt to predictably adapt the biblical accounts of creation under today's scientific assumptions is not without its dangers. Indeed, there are some very impressive examples of attempts to formulate it that rely on Genesis 1, but these examples also make clear that it is important to intentionally retain the biblical accounts in their original ancient language and thus hear what they have to say to us.[140] Herein lies the appropriateness of the Barthian distinction between the area of biblically based creation accounts and the results of scientific research. He rejects the notion that what we believe to know from the source of scientific knowledge or psychoanalytical insight is still fitted with the ornament of biblical language and thus given a certain religious dignity. The biblical message must remain free to challenge the results of scientific observation. Thus, in order to give it emphasis by way of a play on words, it is not so much our "conclusions" that are important in view of the prehistorical course of events but rather our "initiative" with regard to what we understand of nature and humankind.

If one were to briefly summarize in several basic sentences what these reports say, then four observations emerge that preserve the individual passages of the biblical texts while outlining important connecting points with fundamental questions posed by today's science.

(1) Our world is an ordered whole because God's good, creating will has caused it to be and has directed it thus. Accordingly, the basis is laid for a basic trust afforded by faith in creation—even in view of the ambivalence of nature, which we experience both as friendly to life and as life threatening. The fact that we are able to reliably interpret the order of nature through so-called natural laws is the result of the ordered creating action of God and the expression of his loyalty and constancy. For, since there is

intelligent life on the earth, and we, with certain limitations, can understand what happens in the cosmos, there is an indication of "the work of an intentional creator."[141]

(2) Our world was created as the space for life in all of its fullness. God wills life in its variety of levels. The life span of the universe and of our planets is a visible expression that God is friendly to life. Human existence is an integrated component of this fullness of life and has been given the task to maintain and protect what has been created.

(3) God has placed humans in a unique relationship to themselves. The relationship of human beings to God belongs to their essence—whether they know it or not. Here is where their worth lies, in addition to their responsibility. At the same time, it is the tragedy and the guilt of humans that their self-knowledge includes a boundary violation over against God, thus destroying their heretofore unbroken community with God. The fact that evil in the world comes as a result of the transgression of humankind is not a causal explanation for certain biological phenomena like sickness or death or the fight for survival. As "theological etiology," the stories of the creation and the Fall of humanity are directed toward founding a basis for humanity's responsibility before God himself and toward creation, the knowledge of humanity's guilty involvement in the evil of this world, and the longing for an unbroken relationship to God and his creation.[142]

(4) Without expressly stating it, the ancient stories say that what happened at the beginning is not simply a historically verifiable stage of human history that can be proved by virtue of facts and fossils. They are a "utopian recollection" that shows how God had intended the world, even if what we read from the history of nature appears to take the form of another language. Faith in God the Creator is thus at the same time faith in the redeemer.[143]

Our view is thus expanded beyond the story of creation, but in a more narrow sense. We have already seen that dialogue with nature sheds a stronger light on the *creatio continua*, as is the case in Genesis 1–3. However, although Genesis 1 primarily depicts God's creation "at the beginning" as complete, it would be wrong to regard what is told here as only in the past. The "first seven days of creation" represent a kind of time-compressed model of events, which for today's observation of nature, the history of the universe, and our earth continues to unfold up until today. What was created "at the beginning" also describes what God had determined to be the goal of his creation.[144] The fact that this aspect of biblical faith in creation is not foreign is represented by the verses on creation in the Psalms and Deutero-Isaiah. In particular, the identification of divine wisdom as the creative life force, which from the beginning defines the creative activity of God and also presents his will for humankind's path in the service of faith in creation, includes the original event as well as humankind's history (compare Spr. 8:22).

Here the early Jewish identification of the Torah as the life-saving order for the people of God connects with the reigning life-serving order of the cosmos. This identification is the background of the significance of the circle as described in the Qumran calendar and was found later in synagogues in examples portraying the circle of animals as an image for God's created cosmic order.

For early Christianity it was decisive that Christ was identified with the creating wisdom of God (compare 1 Cor. 8:6; Col. 1:15). This has its fullest expression in the *logos* theology in the prologue in John's Gospel. Here ideas from Hellenistic Judaism are adopted, especially those found in Philo, which connect the Old Testament conviction that God created this creation through his living word (Ps. 33:6; Gen. 1) with the stoic view of *logos* as divine "world reason," which in turn gives the cosmos its good order. This creating and continually order-creating *logos* is understood as God's essence as directed toward the world and humanity, and became man in the person of Jesus of Nazareth. It was thus brought near to humankind under the conditions of being human as the fullness of divine presence "full of grace and truth." That which created the world has also borne its suffering and overcome it. The fact that through and in Jesus Christ all things are created (1 Cor. 1:6; Col. 1:15-17) is no mythological description of the coworking of a second divine being at creation; it is a witness to the unity of God with creation and its salvation.

Stephen Hawking says at the end of his book *A Brief History of Time* that the discovery by physicists of a sought-after "unified field theory" would finally mean the triumph of human reason— "for then we would know the mind of God." It was the deep conviction of the early Christians that in Jesus Christ we know "the mind of God" as well as God's plan and the intention that holds together creation and salvation.

However, this once again poses a central question about the idea of God, which is connected with the knowledge of God as the Creator and to the dialogue with scientific research. Primarily, this connection calls for a revision of the conventional idea of God. Thus writes James S. Trefil: "I myself feel better with the idea of a God who created the physical laws, which resulted in the existence of our great world, than with the idea of an old-fashioned God, who laboriously had to form one piece at a time."[145] Paul Davies places a different emphasis as one who has occupied himself with the God question more than many other scientists. The scientific view "makes the idea of a creator God irrelevant, but doesn't exclude an all-encompassing spirit that exists as a part of a unique physical universe: a natural god instead of a supernatural one."[146] Jantsch states something more radical and simple: "God . . . is evolution."[147]

Hans-Rudolf Stadelmann has attempted to make such claims more theologically precise within the framework of pantheistic concepts, but they come off very complicated anyway:

> God is the transcendent, immanent spirit, the all-encompassing creative spiritual principle, in whom through the cosmic evolution of energy over matter and life is increasingly concretized as spirit in the world as his "creation" and inhabits all that is in the world, and manifests himself so in the material and spiritual structures of the world, and thus is recognizable to humans as his self-conscious images.[148]

With all these attempts, we must also consider the argument of Hoimar von Ditfurth who warns evangelical theology against emptying the concept of God through semantic illusions and conceptual tautologies in the course of trying to avoid conflict to such an extent that "the boundary between that of a 'living God' and a contrived atheism becomes increasingly faint."[149]

For this reason many theologians in recent years have turned to a trinitarian creation theology.[150] They reject the idea of a purely external-to-the-world, timeless, all-powerful God, an idea that leads theologically—as well as in discussion with natural science—to an unending *aporia*. They connect faith in God as the sovereign

Creator of the "All" with the conviction that the Creator through his *logos* created this world and its development from the inside out, and that in the incarnation he places limits on what is created as well as on suffering, redesigning this world through the action of his spirit in humanity and in creation. This perspective can also support God the Creator as God who is love, and it recognizes his love as the basic creating power—as "the mind of God." God has created everything because he seeks out the beloved other.[151]

However, at this point we have gone beyond the interpretation of the early account and must return to our topic in the next chapters.

CHAPTER TWO

POWER AND HISTORY— THE FIRST STEPS (4:1–6:4)

The history of humankind continues. More precisely, it begins now. With the beginning of sexual propagation, subsequent generations were set in motion, a state of affairs that was determinative and constitutive for the course of human history. The next chapter of Genesis relates the early history of these successive generations. Genesis 4 essentially follows in the footsteps of the early priestly writings and relays in 4:1-16 the drama of fratricide, which also plays out into the second generation. Genesis 4:17-26 continues with the story of Cain's deed, including commentary on the development of human culture and human community. Chapter 5 again takes up the path of priestly writings and relates, in a list spanning ten generations, the descendants of Adam stemming from the line of Seth, the third son of Adam and Eve. Finally, 6:1-4 tells of the remarkable intrusion from the realm of the divine into the world of humans—a world upon which God himself sets a limit. This section then leads into the story of the flood.

1. The Consequences of Sin—Cain's Fratricide (4:1-16)

In the phrase "Adam knew Eve, his wife" we encounter one of the most important biblical phrases denoting sexual union and procreation. It is not used to avoid explicit sexual language but is an expression of the very personal nature of human sexuality.[1] Procreation is not a result of sin but a consequence of the work of creation, which the priestly writings have described by the phrase "be fruitful and multiply."

Procreation, pregnancy, and birth are mentioned briefly and as such the natural course of human procreation is portrayed. Yet what happens here is a miracle, which Eve describes with an exclamation that hides a play on words with the name of her first son, Cain. *Qanah* means "beget," and Eve says that she has brought forth or "procured" a man, one of the human species, "with the help of the Lord" (in the sense of "together with the Lord"). Two events are merged together here. One is the biological connection between procreation and birth, in which the motherhood of the woman plays a conveying or "cocreating" role, and the other is the theological connection retained in memory that children are a gift from God—even if through biological means. Here nature and grace are legitimately connected.

In verse 2 a second son is born and a new relationship is established: Cain gets a brother. His name, Abel, is not interpreted. However, the Hebrew-speaking person hears meaning in it even if it is not explicitly mentioned: *häbäl* means "breath" or "transience." *Nome nest omen* ("the name is everything"), even for the Israelites. Thus, the name of the firstborn stands for the sign of life as it is offered through the gift of procreation, while the name of the second indicates the reduction of life and loss—the transience of human life, which causes loss of community with God who is the source of life.

Even in the choice of profession there is differentiation of human work. One son was a farmer, the other a shepherd—a basic division of work since the beginning of humanity (at least since the end of the period of man as hunter and gatherer). In the region of Israel and Mesopotamia there was, because of the proximity of the arable land and steppes regions, farming and herding over thousands of years, a fact that often led to conflicts owing to changes in pastureland.

In verses 3-6 both brothers bring a sacrifice to God. This is assumed to be naturally appropriate without having to mention a command to do so. The Hebrew word for "sacrifice" that is used here is also very general and nonspecific: *minchah* means "gift," and here it means a gift for God, by which the person expresses his thanks and honor. In the case of Abel, it is expressly mentioned that it has to do with the "sacrifice of first fruits." The fruit of the acre and the firstborn of the herd is brought to God, the giver of all gifts, as a sacrifice. To do this is clearly understood as a part of human existence, so that no further reason is required.

However, then things get tense. The narrator says casually, "The Lord looked with favor on Abel and his offering, but on Cain and his offering he did not look with favor." (Here we have the vocabulary used in the unified translation, whereas the Lutheran translation brings out the meaning: "And the Lord looked graciously on Abel and his offering, but he did not look graciously on Cain and his offering.")

The narrator does not explain two important things that we would like to know. First, why did God look on Abel and his offering and not on Cain and his offering? Second, how did Cain find this out? Of course, the story gives relatively satisfactory information for the interpretation of both questions.

Therefore, regarding the first question:

- The story designates the offering of animals as more valuable and more pleasing to God.
- Abel's offering was given with more love, which one may derive from the rather more detailed portrayal of his offering.
- Abel's attitude was the correct one. It has to do with God's acceptance and refusal not of the offering but of the person who brings it. ("The Lord looked on Abel and his offering.") Accordingly, Hebrews 11:4 says: "By faith Abel offered God a better sacrifice than Cain did."

If one reads the text of Genesis 4 literally, then it appears to be very important for the point of the story that there is no obvious basis for God's acceptance or refusal.

With regard to the second question, there are ancient traditions that have been found primarily among the plastic arts. The smoke of Abel's offering reached above, while that of Cain's did not. Others assume that Abel's herds would have received God's blessing because they were worth more.

However, nothing in the story is said about this. It mentions only in passing that Cain knew the fact and then relates how he reacted to it. This is told clearly and with matchless brevity; translated literally, "Cain was very angry and his face was downcast." Great anger and deep disappointment is a mixture that causes many murderous conflicts. It stems from the frustration that something that we hold to be self-evident is denied us and sickens us deeply, and from such a sickness springs aggression.

Perhaps we may still conclude something from the dissimilarity of the brothers. The carrier of hope of the family, the progressive farmer, is spurned; the person in the shadows, who lives on the edge of the culture, who protects small domestic animals, and whose name means "nothing" is elevated. What injustice! But at the same time how characteristic of God!

In this situation God speaks to Cain. However, he does not say what we (and perhaps also Cain) would have expected. He does not talk about why he has seen Abel and his offering and has not seen Cain and his offering. He also does not say that although it does not seem like it, Cain is just as important to him as Abel. But the fact that God addresses Cain shows that he is not lost from God's sight and that Cain is still important to him. He asks Cain, "Why are you angry? Why is your face downcast?" God knows what is wrong with Cain, but asks Cain, after the fact, whether his reaction was appropriate or whether he could have dealt with the situation in another way.

Unfortunately, the Hebrew text in verse 7, which relates what God says to Cain, is difficult to understand and thus also difficult to translate. Relying on Horst Seebass, I translate: "If you do what is right, will you not be accepted? But if you do not do what is right, sin is crouching at your door; it desires to have you, but you must master it."[2]

The first key question of this text is: what do "if you do what is right" and "if you do not do what is right" mean? May interpreters understand this in the sense of "when you cause right" or "when you do not cause right" (thus, the universal translation, while the Luther translation says, "when you are pious"). Here, however, a moral judgment of the situation is involved that is not intended in the narrative (thus, Claus Westermann, discussing verse 7, also understands this as a retrospective rationalization of the event).[3]

However, the range of meaning of "doing good" is clearly greater at this juncture. It has to do not only with the ethical good but with successful action. Thus, loosely translated: "If things go well for you, then you can be happy and confident. If, however, things do not go well for you, then sin crouches like a demon at the door of your life and seeks to rule your life, but you are to master it."[4]

For the first time, the word *sin* is used in the Bible and is simultaneously introduced with a double meaning. On the one hand, it is "loss," concrete misconduct with respect to a continuing communal relationship and the neglect of one's own life goal.[5] On the other hand, it is also a demonic power that wants to gain control over the life of a person. However, the person is constructed so as to be able to rule over this power.[6]

Basically, Genesis 4:1-16 is a "story of sin" that in many respects runs parallel to Genesis 3 but in which now the problem is brought to the level of a "concept."

Genesis 3 speaks of temptation in terms of the unknown possibilities of life that entice one from the other side of the prohibition. It speaks of a desire that is inflamed by the anxiety of being prevented from acquiring life's fullness and of the inability to trust in God when that trust is called into question by external forces. It has to do with the relationship to God, to oneself, and to the living world as a whole.

Genesis 4:1-6 speaks of temptation as being a result of feeling held back and not allowed to have hope or to expect success in life because it has been given to another person. It has to do with the relationship to the "brother"—that is, to the neighbor. This is the experience of limitations and the threat of failure that lurks like a demonic power at the door of life. However, humanity is not delivered up to this threat without weapons. God empowers humans with the courage to rule over temptation and sin.

However, Cain does not allow himself to have a discussion with God; he does not speak about what moves him and burdens him. Instead, he remains all alone with his anger and his disappointment. He talks to Abel, but Abel has nothing to say to him. It may be the result of an old mistake that the Masoretic text is missing the command "Let's go out to the field," which our translation interprets according to the ancient texts of the Samaritan tradition.[7]

However, it is nevertheless symbolically significant that the communication between the brothers is broken.

Cain does not seek any help in his conflict and so it escalates. He kills his brother Abel, and thus the first murder takes place. Then God speaks to Cain again (v. 9) and asks him, "Where is your brother Abel?" The question conforms to God's question in 3:9, "Where are you?" in which God asks Adam where he is hiding.

Cain lies, "I don't know." And then he gets impertinent, "Am I my brother's keeper?" Perhaps here there is a play on words concerning the profession of his brother—namely, "Do I have to look out for sheep?" The defense strategy of Cain compared to that of Adam in Genesis 3 shows how much humankind's relationship to God has already gone bad. Cain paid very close attention to his brother because it was his perception that God was going to accept Abel and his offering. However, now that Cain has killed Abel, he tries to pass off the responsibility.

It is still essentially true: each and every person is responsible to God (compare Rom. 14:8-12). However, at the same time it is also the case that people are responsible to one another. The command to love one's neighbor as oneself is cited in Leviticus 19:17-18 as the opposite of the law of wrath and revenge against one's neighbor, and includes the critical coresponsibility for the deeds of others. It may be a general human observation that this responsibility is most heavily rejected when we have transgressed against another person.

God confronts Cain with the reality of his deed. The question "What have you done?" (compare also 3:13) basically does not require an answer. The blood of the murder victim cries out from the ground; what has happened cannot be fixed. As in the cry for help of the oppressed and besieged, so now also the blood of the murdered person cries out to God.

This is an axiom of the Old Testament's interpretation of life, but it does not have to do with how Cain or God judges the situation. Spilled blood—destroyed life—becomes the power of a calamity that continues on. The question of the possibility of sin hinges on this point. How, then, can the disaster that occurred be handled?

Nothing is said about this at first. God's reaction establishes the consequences of Cain's deed. The curse that God gives, which is directed right at Cain this time, is also here the "curse of the bad deed." "Now you are under a curse and driven from the ground." The curse for the farmer Cain is such that the ground of life is taken away from him because this ground has now been destroyed through the spilling of Abel's blood. Cain is not allowed to stay. Perhaps this form of punishment is a reflection of the method used in early social settings to avenge a murder within a clan through expulsion from the community, which was tantamount to a death sentence.[8] Expulsion from the ground corresponds to the banishment from paradise and is still the harsher punishment since it seems to take away the foundation of life.

Cain finally reacts and says to Yahweh, "My punishment is more than I can bear." In the Luther Bible it is noted that Luther originally translated this as, "My sin is greater than can be forgiven." Interestingly enough, both translations are possible. This has to do with the fact that the Hebrew concept of 'awôn used here can mean "transgression" (of a deed), "sin" (and its guilty character), or "punishment" (the consequence of the deed).

The 'awôn is "a living effective burden" and at the same time a death-conveying reality that has to be borne no matter what.[9] It is either "punishment" for the doer or God carries it in place of the guilty person—and then it is "forgiveness." The first is valid for our connection: Cain changed his own life through taking the life of his brother. That is the nature of guilt and at the same time punishment, which Cain has to carry. He knows this. He also sees that his exile from the ground means exile from community with God and that he will be rootless and homeless—free as the birds but without any rights. Anyone can kill him—the dying will continue. That is the problem to which Cain refers. It has to do with the portrayal of his fate and with his unexpressed wish not so much regarding his own individual fate, or for milder conditions for his own person, but for the basic protection of rights, even for the perpetrator of the deed. Cain "retains before Yahweh the freedom to request a limitation on the previously administered consequences of guilt . . . because only thus is Yahweh's will for peace and justice fulfilled."[10]

Accordingly, the murderer Cain receives from God a sign of protection that prevents him from having to live in a lawless environment. The announcement of sevenfold vengeance is a symbolic strengthening and does not mean sevenfold blood revenge;

indeed, this is also placed out of reach. "Cain, the murderer of his brother, stands under the punishment of God; but no man has the right to interfere with God's punishment."[11] Both aspects are designated by the "mark of Cain."

The story in verse 14 describes in an interesting way the other people into whose hands Cain may fall. Perhaps this is an indication that this story originally stems from another context, because it does not involve either of the first sons of the first human pair. However, those who placed this story in its current context saw no reason to change anything, and the ancient narrators ostensibly had their own logic. For them it was not about the story of the first family but about the early history of humankind. They knew about the paradigmatic character of stories and therefore did not change them over such inconsequential matters.

A short note closes the story. Cain must go from God's presence ("Cain went out from the LORD's presence") and live in the land of "Nod." This is not a geographical place, but a symbolic play on words in the Hebrew—namely, the land of "instability." Just as Eden denotes a "positive idea," so also Nod is a "negative symbol."[12] It ostensibly lies east of Eden where, in 3:24, the cherubim guard the entrance to God's garden. It is a life far away from God, a meaning that John Steinbeck had very much in mind when he titled his novel *East of Eden*.

The end of the story again underscores the parallels to the paradise narrative. Both stories are about the Fall as a result of sin (even if the word *sin* only appears in the second story), although the first portrays the failure of humanity and the resulting break with God still entirely in narrative form. In both, it has to do with the collapse of human beings at the basic level of their existence.[13]

Genesis 3 poses the question, How do humans deal with the fact that their knowledge and abilities have had limits set on them while still being aware that God's knowledge and being transcend their own knowledge and being? Can people respect the fullness of their own ability to learn and contribute, and at the same time respect the limits set by God? Or do they want to be "like God"— that is, put themselves in God's place? The story of Adam and Eve shows how people are thus destroyed—and they remain in their failed state as a type of community of a similar fate, alienated from one another and yet still tied to one another.

Genesis 4 poses the question, How do people behave when they know that their neighbor—their brother or sister—has had more success and recognition than they themselves have had? Will they "be like the others" and do away with their neighbor in order to step into his or her place? That does not always lead to murder. A physical death sentence is bad enough, but the fact that this process not only plays out between individuals, but also in envy and hate between groups and nations, goes without saying.

Discriminations emerge where there is meaningful work and diversity, thus erupting into rivalries with deadly consequences. Sin not only has an existential dimension but a social dimension as well. Cain and Abel influenced the fate of humankind as much as did Adam and Eve, but now clearly in the positions of perpetrator and victim.[14]

2. Aggression and Sin—A Preliminary Perspective

For the first time in the story of Cain and Abel we meet the phenomenon of aggression. Aggression describes an important, but not unproblematic, reaction of animals and people. In aggression there is the power to combat danger and to engage the enemy, which is similar to defending oneself, one's own group, or one's descendants. However, aggression is also something with a goal—destructive behavior against another person that harms the person or kills her or him. This destructive behavior often involves violence for no reason, or violence far beyond the factual cause.

In analyzing this phenomenon, we can distinguish between internal and external aggression. Internal aggression has to do either directly or indirectly with dominance. The story of Cain's murder of Abel undoubtedly has to do with internal aggression. This is the decisive ethical problem, although such aggressive behavior against other living beings is ethically in no way neutral and, in the early narrative of Genesis 9, is forged into a theme.

Aggression as such is thus not evil; it is comparable to sexuality as one of the basic powers of human and animal life. The story of Cain and Abel agrees with the results of modern behavioral research that says that aggression is caused by a threat to dominance. It is introduced as a power that, when it overtakes the person, becomes sin because it destroys the relationship to the neighbor and, among other things, the relationship to life. It is the job of human beings to control this power instead of allowing it to overtake them.

In his book *On Aggression*, Konrad Lorenz has suggested that the internal type of aggression serves an indispensable function for the conservation of the species. Its detrimental effects to the conserva- tion of the species were, as a rule, prevented through rituals of deflection, and particularly through a very reliably functioning death inhibition when it came to internal fights for dominance in a group. A paramount example for this was the observation that in disagreements between rival wolves the lower one offered its throat to the other as a sign of capitulation, upon which the more dominant wolf would never bite to kill. Lorenz suggested that this death inhibition had also originally been in humans but had dete- riorated through the conditions of progressive civilization and with disastrous consequences, especially as ever more destructive weapons were placed at humanity's disposal. Since attempts to oppress aggression are not effective, Lorenz suggests that they are worked through and controlled by other means, especially through the use of surrogate objects (as for example in competitive sports).[15] More recent research, however, has shown that the assumed death inhibition in animals is, in general terms, much less often the case—not with wolves and, in particular, not with pri- mates. In chimpanzees, observers have recorded deadly kinds of disagreements among relatives connected with cannibalism as well as wars among family groups, which are typical forms of untamed aggression.[16] Volker Sommer comments on the change in thinking that is reflected here, in the following:

> It remains to be asked, what actually led to the mistake to defend the honor of animals and to all kinds of specious assumptions that only man is capable of killing a member of his own species? . . . The blanket acquittal of animals may relate to the Christian teaching on sin and a subliminal arrogance that only concedes to humans the capability for reason: only that which is in image of God can have the power of reason over its actions and lifestyle, even if it rejects good in favor of evil, since that is attributed to the power of sin. As soon as the inhabitants of Eden began to think, they were guilty, bad people. And after the expulsion from para- dise their viciousness increased: Cain's fratricide followed shortly

afterward. It should not absolve us ethically, from the point of view of the history of evolution, even if the Fall into sin had taken place long before Adam and Eve walked the earth.[17]

On the one hand, this observation places us yet again before the problem that the picture of a world before the Fall—a world without suffering, struggle, and death, as it appears to be in the early accounts—is refuted by biological research. The great "disruption" evidently goes much deeper and begins much earlier.

On the other hand, humankind's ethical responsibility is not removed nor is murder some unavoidable law of nature. It is noteworthy that even scientists who agree with evolutionary biology refer at this point to the categorical difference between animals and humans. Hans Mohr writes: "The evil in early human evolution is the 'so-called evil.' . . . It defies moral categories. 'The actual evil' begins with people who, even in freedom and responsibility, still push against these norms. The actual evil—the sin—comes from the discrepancy between being and wanting, which did not exist in the preliberation phase of evolution."[18] The warning about "nature's conclusions" that makes nature a model for our ethics is an important topic for discussion.[19]

With similar enthusiasm, Richard Dawkins writes:

> We have the power to defy the selfish genes of our birth and, if necessary, the selfish memes of our indoctrination. We can even discuss ways of deliberately cultivating and nurturing pure, disinterested altruism—something that has no place in nature, something that has never existed before in the whole history of the world. We are built as gene machines and cultured as meme machines, but we have the power to turn against our creators. We, alone on earth, can rebel against the tyranny of the selfish replicators.[20]

However, Edward O. Wilson is more skeptical: "The facts prove that the person, on the basis of this biological predisposition, is ready to accept only a small spectrum of ethical norms."[21]

How this predisposition contributes to our question is disputed. According to Irenäus Eibl-Eibesfeldt, humans are "built for freedom" and disposed by an "innate norm filter that prohibits death."[22] In addition, Richard Leakey writes that he does not believe that "power is an inborn character of humanity; I think it is rather an unfortunate reaction to certain circumstances."[23] In contrast, Volker Sommer writes: "The *natural being* of man appears to have no natural predilection hindering him to kill . . . an effective counterimpulse we could only expect from the *cultural being* of man."[24]

The challenge of the story of Cain and Abel is thus, in view of our discussion, contained in God's request to Cain not to allow himself to be overcome by the powers that threaten him, but to control those powers and himself. Accordingly, the person who has chosen the knowledge of good and evil also has responsibility toward God and the community. For the narrator, "Human autonomy in all its ambivalence has become the inevitable sign of man postparadise."[25] Autonomy, as such, is not sin, and neither is sin considered an unconquerable power.[26] But at the same time, the early account presents the fact that from the beginning humans have failed to accept this responsibility. It is envy that causes the aggression that is then not ruled, and envy is nothing other than the anxiety of coming up short compared to another person. Thus, in our story anxiety about oneself is indirectly exposed as the root of sin. Therefore, the collapse of human society also causes alienation from God and vice versa. In reconciliation with God and in salvation, anxiety would—through a newly given trust—be the basis for an appropriate dealing with aggression and for the healing of human community.[27]

3. Culture and Power in Humanity's Beginnings (4:17-26)

The early account follows a piece of early priestly writing, and in so doing it pursues, to a certain extent, the story of Cain and his descendants. Even the person for whom the "face of the LORD" is gone and who now lives "on the other side of Eden," far in the East, does not entirely disappear. It is important to remember that this person also belongs to the story of humanity.

And the story of humanity continues on in the same way as it did at the beginning. As with Adam in 4:1, so now it is Cain: "Cain lay with his wife, and she became pregnant and gave birth to Enoch" (v. 17). At this juncture, the narrator is not interested in how Cain got a wife. He reports on the descendants of the first human pair and is not surprised that there are other people too. A similar dual view of things could also be construed in the report that Cain built a city, which he then named for his son. A city is something that one builds for many people! However, where they come from is not a question the narrator asks. The wanderers and refugees—those uprooted from their ancestral ground—build a city for his son! Farming and cities belong together and continue to coexist in a tension-filled relationship. The fact that the building of the city is connected with Cain sends a signal to the hearers and readers. City planning is an ancient art going back to the beginning of humanity. However, the building of cities had its origins external to the direct early history of Israel.[28]

Very briefly the story names the firstborn sons of the next generation, extending to Lamech, the seventh son of Adam. Here the account reveals a clear break and inserts two very different notations—as if it were appropriate—upon reaching the seventh generation, in order to construct a brief yet temporary balance.

In the first parenthetical notation we discover something about the direct descendants of Lamech. The fact that Lamech had two wives is a fact that is not criticized and is merely recorded as the result of human history. Adah, the wife who is named first, bore Jabal and Jubal. The former of these is the father of the nomadic tribes and the latter is the father of musicians, from among whom the lyre and flute players are named in particular. In addition, they are the wandering people who are mentioned along with the nomads.[29]

Even the second named wife, Zillah, had two children. Tubal-cain is a smith of ore and iron, and thus introduces the phase of the special craftsman. From a cultural-historical perspective, the smith also belongs to the wandering workers who offered their highly specialized abilities among the settlements and campsites of the nomads. The development of ore (i.e., bronze) and ironwork is thus projected back onto a common beginning.

The sister of Tubal-cain is Naamah, or "sweet." She is not a bearer of any cultural achievement, yet both she and her name do not go unmentioned. She is worthy of mention as a person and as a wife, even if her use for the future is not motivated by the implementation of a cultural good. (In general, this narrator demonstrates that he names women; compare 11:29-30.)

This short note does not represent the core of a cultural history of humanity, but only sheds light on the beginning and meaning of a "wandering people" who were perhaps found not only geographically on the edge of society but also in the family tree of the Canaanites. While still signaling a positive assessment of their cultural development, their significance is not highlighted. It is not reported by "divine invention," which would otherwise introduce such an elevated status, but their development is also not placed in a negative light. In addition, the fact that the descendants of Cain produce these achievements does not disqualify the achievements from the start. Moreover, in the culture and in the power that it affords there lurks the potential for misuse. Although the subsequent account of Lamech's song of revenge indicates no direct connection to what precedes it, there is still an indication of some kind of connection.

Lamech's "song of victory" is a song that he sings to his wives. Women functioned in the ancient tradition as heralds of deeds of war. In Lamech's song, a self-appointed hero boasts of his deeds and describes a kind of aggressiveness that, in every aspect, is boundless. The principle of "adequate recompense" ("eye for an eye, tooth for a tooth"), which looks to us like an expression of unbridled revenge and which in the ancient world helped moderate aggression, is broken here willingly and randomly: to kill a man because of a wound and a youth because of a bruise was an expression of uncontrolled aggression. Thus, the formula protecting Cain becomes a license for an unbounded revenge ("seven times seven" is the expression for something limitless; compare its positive use in the contrasting text in Matt. 18:22).[30] Here the culture swings into a deadly self-display. In visual terms, plowshares become swords in order to increase the effectiveness of death, and although these verses are related without commentary or censorship, they reflect the image of humanity "on the other side of Eden"—great in cultural achievements, but also limitless in inhumane self-assertion.[31]

The implied criticism of the story is reflected in that, at this point, the story now switches to tell of the new beginnings of a line of human history stemming from the birth of Adam and Eve's third son. Eve names him Seth (linguistically similar to "sapling" or "youth") and says: "God has granted me another child in place of

78

Abel, since Cain killed him." Once more a reference is made to Abel—not because Cain was declared dead, but because God has chosen the "youth." The history of the elect is going to continue with Seth, and the story of election is also the story of humanity—clearly illustrated by the name of Seth's son Enoch, a name which, like Adam, means "man." With Seth and his descendants a new line begins that is led by God. This is underscored through a brief remark that is difficult to interpret: "At that time [people] began to call on the name of the LORD."

Clearly, the narrator does not share the conventional interpretation of the Elohist tradition in Exodus 3:14, and especially those interpretations represented by the priestly tradition after Exodus 6:3 that hold to the conviction that the name of God as Yahweh was first revealed in Israel by Moses. The editing of the Pentateuch has also not removed this discrepancy. People knew of the true God from the beginning, and so also the true name of God was known from the beginning. It is not once claimed that this was only true for the human line that descended from Seth and Enoch. However, after the immediate community between God and humanity was broken by the behavior of Adam and Cain, a new possibility of being in relationship to God began: that of calling upon his name.

Two elements are important here: (1) the Bible does not recognize an "early religion" that believes in something other than calling upon the one God who Israel knows by the name of Yahweh, whose being and name have remained constant from the beginning.[32] And (2) the essence of the relationship of humans to God is very simple and described simply by saying that he can be called upon by name. Nothing is said about sacrifice or any other forms of worship; the core of the relationship to God is to call upon his name. After the loss of the immediate "idyllic" connection to God, this is the only possibility of coming into contact with him. Accordingly, this is the basic definition of the relationship of Abram to God (Gen. 12:8), and again in Joel 2:32 it is expected at the universal end times: "And everyone who calls on the name of the LORD will be saved."

Interestingly enough, in this regard, the early account nowhere mentions the question of other gods, although disagreements with the creation myths of other religions could have led to this.

Nevertheless, the story of the beginning is the story of the one God who acts in creation and who, through creation, speaks to humankind.

4. The Continuity of Generations from Adam to Noah (5)

With the mention of Seth and his son Enoch, the early history gains a new perspective. It continues in chapter 5, and only then when using the priestly writings. However, they do not comprise an actual story in connection to the creation story but rather a detailed account of the descendants of Adam and Seth who serve to bridge the time span between Adam and Noah. It is the first of the so-called genealogies, which many Bible readers do not like but which are very important for the biblical narrative.

The new beginning is marked by a title: "This is the written account of Adam's line" (*toledot*, meaning "begotten").[33] The chapter begins with a short summary of what has happened so far in terms of the creation of humankind. It relies on 1:27 and emphasizes three hallmarks of God's activity:

- God has created humans in his image.
- God has created them as man and woman.
- God has blessed them and given them the name "human." "Humanity" is imparted to humankind by God and is imprinted with the sign of blessing—the promise of fullness of life, which God gives to humans from the beginning as part of creation.

Then the list of the subsequent generations follows. They are boring for the reader of the Bible in their monotonous similarity. However, this fact is in itself very impressive. The following basic scheme is consequently maintained:

X was N years old when he had Y.
After he had Y, he lived another P years and had other sons and daughters.
Altogether X lived R years and then he died.

Life runs according to the same rhythm. The pulse of the generations thus defines the history of humankind. The result is strongly patrilineal, even though daughters are mentioned with some regularity.

With the beginning of this list, the concept of Adam is relegated to the proper name for an individual, with details about life span. Even so, in verse 2, in many translations, man and woman are still mentioned collectively as "Adam" or "man."

From verse 3 on, Adam is then the representative of the first generations in a list that encompasses ten generations up to Noah. The series of generations describes an entire epoch—namely, that of the epoch between creation and the flood. Only three people break up the monotony of the information through incidental descriptions. In the case of Seth, it is stressed that Adam conceived him "in his own likeness and in his image." Thus, the same formula is used as in Genesis 1:26, where God decides to make humans in his own likeness. The worth of human beings that comes from being made in God's likeness is handed down from generation to generation. Moreover, the son of the first man has a human countenance and in it is mirrored the ongoing basic definition of being human. Although the reference to subsequent generations is not repeated, it establishes a sign for the history of humankind: the continuity of the blessing of God and the definition of humankind are protected. The Bible thus prefers to speak of the "original worth" of humans rather than speak of "original sin."

The next amazing thing is announced as occurring in the seventh generation. In two places it says of Enoch: "He walked with God." Clearly, a very close relationship to God is described, which is the result of action and being in accord with God's will. The same thing was said only of Noah (6:9; the command to Abraham contains a similar formulation in 17:10). The priestly writings do not contain a story of the Fall. However, in their narratives it is clear that what is fundamentally determinative and should be the content of human life has become the exception to the rule. For the reader, the final version of the early story highlights that what in paradise was played out in full community with God is still not entirely removed from human life as a possibility. There is indeed one who lives life step-by-step in accord with God and breaks the cycle of birth, procreation, and death. Enoch's fate is, however, difficult to determine. Literally, the narrative says, "Then he was no more, because God took him away." If one were to explain his story historically or psychologically, it would be fair to assume that in ancient times people had heard of a particularly pious man who had suddenly disappeared. In reflecting on it, it was explained that God took him to Godself or—as in the interpretation of 2 Kings 2:3, 5, 9 (where the same words are used)—God has taken him away.

Whatever the roots of these small accounts (there were also Sumerian Babylonian myths that included the motif of the rapturing of an ancient pious man),[34] in its current form it primarily has symbolic meaning. The seventh generation and the relatively short life span of Enoch consist of 365 years, as many years as the sun calendar has days. The person who has lived the closest to God lives the shortest, but at the same time lives a complete life span. God takes him to Godself. This is relayed in a very uneventful way and is also not connected with a speculative look at the other world, as is later required in the apocalypse of Enoch.[35] The one "who walks with God" reaches his goal.

The third parenthetical notation is found in the birth of Noah. Just as with the sons of Adam and Eve, there is a formula for naming. His father "named him Noah and said, 'He will comfort us in the labor and painful toil of our hands caused by the ground the LORD has cursed.'" This verse stems from the Jahwist story line, as is shown by the allusion to 3:17-19 and the use of the name Yahweh. The name of Noah (Hebrew: *Noach*) is connected with the verb *nacham pi*, or "comfort," from the etymology of the word for "people." In terms of content, there is a lot of discussion of the growing of grapes and making of wine, which Noah undertook after 9:20. It is not entirely clear if the story takes a positive or a negative view of it; but apparently the tradition did not completely hide the role of wine as a source of joy in life, since it is praised in Psalm 105:15. The curse that God gave to the ground has not robbed it of every blessing. The gift of wine is a sign of that.[36] In any case, all three of Noah's sons are named, which is important for the continuation of the history.

Let us look once more at the entire list. It is important to recognize that it represents a narrative that is constructed from various transmitted elements that have been very artfully combined together into a unified whole. Thus, it is apparent that the series of names also appears to be very similar to the Canaanite family tree in 4:17-22 (Enoch, Irad/Jared, Mahalalel/Mehujaël, Methuselah/Metuschaël, Lamech). Apparently, people knew the names from the ancient times, but put them in a different order.

The manner of counting years is also constructed from various elements. This has been shown by the fact that the traditions all had different ways of counting: there was the method used in the Masoretic texts, whose numbers appear in our Bible translation; the Septuagint method; and that of the Samaritan tradition. The latter is the most interesting. In it, the years of life decrease in relatively consistent fashion from Adam (930 years) to Lamech (653 years), whereas only Noah reaches an age of more than 950 years. In this system, Adam still encounters the young Noah (in the Masoretic system he dies after Lamech's birth), and accordingly the forefathers of Noah die in the year of the flood (and also in it! Here, Jared, Methuselah, and Lamech). The Septuagint has consequently raised the age of procreation and life span, but meanwhile overlooked the fact that according to its chronology Methuselah with his 969 years would have survived the flood (and according to the Masoretic system he died in the year of the flood!).[37]

What do these numbers mean? As astonishing as they are, they are not explained. In retrospect (6:3), it has been shown that the long time span indicates an intense presence of spirit and God's breath of life in human beings. The long decline, as is primarily the case with the Samaritan system, shows the gradual decline of a close relationship to God. However, this may not be viewed as anything more than the consequence of cultural decline, since Enoch, who "walked with God," lived the shortest period of time, which was clearly a very long span of time, even in terms of symbolic numbers. What a superficial reading does not reveal is offered by a more detailed look at the numbers: they indicate a long-term overlapping of generations. Perhaps this is because in the ancient world they not only described individuals but epochs, which for the ancients were still connected to one another in broad terms.[38] The fabric of the genealogical system and its combination of numbers represents the concentration and continuity of human beings and their history in a synchronous as well as diachronous fashion. Human history is "a continuum in time, and yet any individual person in this continuum has his own particular history and fate."[39] At the same time, the portrayal of the successive line of generations represents divine blessing, a fact that is expressly mentioned in 5:2 and is elegantly exemplified by the chain of "generations." The issue of a disturbance is thus delayed until the next chapter.

5. The Sons of God and Supermen (6:1-4)

The next short story belongs to a section of the book of Genesis that is the most difficult to explain. This is partially because of the fact that we do not know the precise meaning of several of the Hebrew words. In addition, the logical connections between the individual elements and meanings of the verses are not very easy to reconstruct.

This anecdote belongs to the early priestly writings (compare v. 3). However, it does not directly connect to previous accounts but begins relatively independently with the description of a new situation: "when men began to increase in number on the earth and daughters were born to them."[40] The perspective of the story broadens: the successive generations of families are no longer at the center. Humanity (Hebrew: *ha 'adam*) has increased on the earth (Hebrew: *'adamah*) and suddenly daughters are of particular concern. Why that is the case is shown in the following: "And the sons of God saw that the daughters of men were beautiful, and they married any of them they chose."

Who are these sons of God?[41] A twofold explanation is critical here. "Sons" in the Semitic language does not mean a physical descendant, but as belonging to an area. "Sons of God" also means belonging to the divine world. The use of the phrase "sons of God" appears especially in the Canaanite world of divinities, for example in Ugaritic. There are many surrogates as well as secondary gods. In the Old Testament there is an expression for beings who have an important function in God's realm (Job 1:6; 2:1; Satan is also included here; 38:7; Psalm 29:1; 89:6). The Psalms also show that the "sons of God" cannot be simply identified with angels, although naturally many connections have been made between both. In Psalm 82:6 the "sons of the highest" are the gods of human beings, with whom God goes to court. That may also be the background here. In the subsequent monotheistic ancient history, this small phrase looms like the tip of an iceberg of disagreement with the surrounding polytheistic environment. The role of these divine beings comprises a theme that was very popular in all of the ancient Orient and also in classical antiquity: the relationship between the gods and human women. Not least, the legitimacy of lordship and power was often sought as the coming of the line of the gods!

The sons of God see that the human daughters are beautiful and take wives from among them. This is stated without any critical undertones, and even with a little bit of pride. The daughters of men are so beautiful that the sons of God find them attractive. The argument of many later interpretations that the women had received their beauty from the angels is foreign to the story, although it also conveys something of the threat that exposes beautiful women to the greediness of men (compare Gen. 26:7).

The implicit criticism of the sons of God appears to lie in the type and kind of man portrayed in action, a nuance that is not communicated in the course of translation: "They married any of whom they chose." The verb *bachar* or "choose, elect," which theologically is the term for "choice" or "election," is used here in the sense of an all-powerful, arbitrary selection. Accordingly, the emphasis is on "any of them," indicating that the sons of God are treated like oriental kings with a harem. They are thus the prototypes of the powerful, and defined by their prowess over others, especially over women. However, their behavior remains remarkably ambivalent in the story because it appears to portray the breaking in of the divine into the lives of humans.

Verse 3 recounts Yahweh's reaction to this situation whose logic, at first, is not very transparent. For, while nothing specifically is said about guilt on the part of the human daughters, God's countermeasure appears to engage humanity (*ha'adam*) as punishment: "Then the LORD said: 'My Spirit will not contend with [humans] forever, for [they are] mortal; [their] days shall be a hundred and twenty years.'"[42]

Here an important line is drawn between the divine and the human. God's spirit, the breath of life, which gives life to humans as well as to all living things (compare Ps. 104:29), will not remain in human beings "forever." Human life has its limits in terms of time. That is what makes it human. As in Genesis 3, the limits of human life and the disappearance of eternal life are not acts of punishment but "the prevention of an eternity that would no longer be permeated by the original human creation, but by evil."[43] Thus, here the statement that humans are "flesh" in contrast to God's spirit is not a negative disqualifier, but assigns to human beings their place among the creatures of the earth.

Verse 4 underscores this with a passage that is again difficult to incorporate into the previous verse: "The Nephilim were on the earth in those days—and also afterward—when the sons of God went to the daughters of men and had children by them. They were the heroes of old, men of renown."

The context and also the second part of this verse are close to what is meant by the Nephilim (giants; compare Num. 13:33) and the heroes of old, meaning the children that were produced from the relationship between the sons of God and the daughters of men. This is also the case in the Luther translation and in the Good News Bible. The original text is not clear; but it is interesting that, here again, the motif of a quasi-divine power is used which, on the one hand, awakens dignified awe ("famous men"), but on the other hand, also awakens fear and terror ("giants").

The theme of this short story is also about those who rule over others and for whom desire and covetousness appear to have no limits. The story shows the threat of the powerful who help themselves without regard for others, even when it has to do with men (and especially with women). And it shows the temptation hidden in wanting divine power and immortality.

In the ancient oriental world and in classical antiquity, there were the powerful who claimed to be descended from the gods and who thus also claimed the right to define their law as divine law. However, the "men"—the heroes of the ancient time—stood under the limits of human existence, as seen in verse 3. They were mortals to whom no honor was due.[44]

Thus, this story is very consciously placed between the story of paradise and the story of the tower of Babel. It has to do with the attempt to want to be God—or to want to be like God. However, in this case it is not through the action of humans but through the breaking in of the designated divinity into the world. The attractive aspect of "being chosen" hides the reality of "being used." The story shows, however, humans in "[their] delivered fate and resulting alienation, which is full of consequences. . . . And [humans do] not cause the roots of all [their] misfortune by [themselves] alone."[45] This unburdens human beings, but without excusing them.

At first glance, the mythological motif of the relationship between the sons of God and the daughters of man places us beyond the attempt to eat from the tree of the knowledge of good and evil. But the danger of perceived empowerment by virtue of a divine power or by "destiny," and the self-indulgence that arises from it, has not disappeared. Recent German history is a horrifying example of this.

The implicit criticism of polytheism, which is suggested by the mention of the sons of God, consists in the polytheistic system's blurring of the boundaries between God and men because of the many levels of its divine world. They represent "crossovers," and as such, are very dangerous for the humanity of the person.

However, God gives saving limitations that become the theme of the story of the tower of Babel. It appears almost to represent a parallel secular account to 6:1-4 (compare Table 3). For, if here it has to do with the attempt to overcome human limitations through connection to divine power, then in the story of Babel it has to do with the overcoming of human limitations through human achievement.

CHAPTER THREE

LAW AND GRACE—
THE CRISIS (6:5–9:17)

The story of the flood, in addition to and following upon the story of the creation of the world and people, comprises the second highpoint of biblical early history. The threat to life on earth through God's judgment, and the wonderful saving of humankind and animals, connected with the divine promise never again to exterminate the earth, represents an early account that almost reaches the level of a second creation story.

Apart from the creation story, it corresponds to the biblical story of humankind's rescue from an annihilating flood—a story that also emerged quite often in the myths and lore of other cultures. This is not only the case for areas in which great floods were always expected, such as in Mesopotamia, but also for areas in which there was not historical substantiation of great floods having occurred.[1] What does this mean for the interpretation of the story of the flood?

1. The Flood as Humanity's Fate

At the story's most basic level, two questions should be distinguished:

1. What relationship exists between the story of the flood and other flood stories in the myths and lore of other people?
2. What relationship exists between the flood story and the flood legend that we have in three different versions

from Mesopotamia and that exhibits many detailed connections to the biblical story?

Many interpreters do not think the first question is very productive, since no connection to a tradition can be established between,
for example, the Aztec or the Polynesian flood stories and the biblical tradition. In his commentary, Claus Westermann presents a
schematic overview of the variations between the many different
traditions and has rightly rejected this view. Indeed, his parallels
among the various cultural circles are impressive, despite existing
differences!

One has tried, using apologetics, to analyze this state of affairs and
to see the broad range of flood stories as the recollection of a global
historical event that affected all of humankind the world over. Thus,
the fact is often reiterated that in almost all regions of the earth, even
in today's arid regions, geological traces of flooding can be found.[2]

However, this represents a misguided attempt to prove the
"truth" of the biblical account. There are not any geological indications of a global flood catastrophe, which would have covered the
entire surface of the earth. Thus, the verses containing the story of
the flood over humanity also carry another truth that, in itself,
makes reference to a historical event in the geological history of our
earth. The story of an early flood that threatened to completely
destroy life on earth, but from which the earth was marvelously
preserved, appears to articulate an "early trauma" in the course of
humanity in which, at the same time, there is perceived the core of
a regained original trust—namely, there is the chance for a new
beginning and a newly won future, even in the face of the threat of
global annihilation.

The relationship between the biblical story of the flood and the
Mesopotamian flood legend is much closer. The latter has been
handed down in three versions: fragments of a Sumarian flood
story, the Babylonian Atram-hasis epic,[3] and the interpolated story
of the Utnapishtim onto the eleventh tablet of the Babylonian
Gilgamesh epic, which is clearly an excerpt developed from the
Atram-hasis story.[4]

In comparing the Mesopotamian versions of the flood story with
the biblical account, it is possible to find some agreement from
among the following motifs:

- The gods' decision to exterminate men
- The decision to save a few select people (including the accoutrements and personal items that a new humanity would need)
- The command to build a rescue ship
- The coming of the flood
- The sending out of birds for information on the receding of the flood
- The offering on the part of those who are saved and the reaction of the gods

These correlations are so strong that it may be assumed that the Mesopotamian stories were known to Israel in literary or even in quite firmly engrained oral form.

Naturally, there are also many differences in detail between the traditions, two of which have particular theological significance.

- In the epic of Atram-hasis, the basis for the decision to annihilate humankind is given: humankind was created to serve the gods and especially to alleviate the work of the lower gods. Now, however, humans had multiplied (compare Gen. 6:1) and with their noisy work had disturbed the gods. They especially disturbed the sleep of higher god Enlil.[5] The plagues sent to decimate humanity—such as plagues of wild animals, starvation, or pestilence—had no long-lasting effect because they were brought on through the deviousness of the well-intentioned, people-friendly god Enki (Ea). Thus, the decision in the council of the gods is to annihilate humankind.
- Here the second essential difference is revealed: the decision to annihilate all of humanity comes from the advice of the gods who are led by Enlil, whereas the decision to save at least a select few is the work of the god Enki (Ea). After the flood, and in council with the gods, Enki (Ea) then claims that the gods need humankind's offerings, and so Enlil's decision is overruled. In the future, the transgressions of humans should not, in general, be avenged and their increase should be controlled—but not by means of annihilation. Various actors in the model of the Polynesian pantheon also portray God's contradictory

behavior in the biblical story of the flood (i.e., regret over the creation of human beings and the resolve to extermi-nate; the decision to save Noah and his family together with all animals; the retraction of the decision to annihi-late). In a monotheistic concept, the conflict of contrasting reactions concerning the behavior of humankind must be played out in the heart of one God.

2. The Literary Sources of the Flood Accounts

In view of these findings, it is almost symbolic that the story of the flood, right up until today, presents a supreme example of how two source writings are woven together into one story. Indeed, in the account of the flood two thematically related stories are placed side-by-side. However, the flood stories in both sources P and J are artfully worked into a single story.[6] Evidence for this is abundant.[7]

A series of events is mentioned in both sources:

The evil of humankind	6:5 J and 6:11-12 P
The decision to annihilate	6:7 J and 6:13 P
The command to go into the ark	7:1-3 J and 6:18-21 P
Going into the ark	7:1 J and 7:13 P
Coming of the flood	7:10 J and 7:11 P
The extermination of all creatures	7:22 J and 7:20-21 P
The end of the flood	8:2b, 3a J and 8:3b-5 P
The promise for the future	8:21b-22 J and 9:1-17 P

In addition, a series of remarkable linguistic and content-related elements emerge, which characterize either one or the other source:

- The name of God in J is Yahweh, and in P is Elohim.
- The name of earth in J is *'adamah*, and in P is *'äräz*.
- In J the number of all pure animals is seven, and among those only one pair is taken into the ark (7:2); and in P pairs of all animals are allowed (6:19; 7:15).
- In J the forty days of rain cause the flood (7:120), and in P they cause the breaking of the floodwaters from over and under the earth (7:110).

- In J we have vague dates (7:4, 10, 12; 8:6-13), and in P exact dates (7:11, 24; 8:3, 5).

The editor worked in such a way that the beginning and the end of the story use larger blocks of the sources (the decision to destroy humankind and the preservation of Noah [6:5-8 J + 6:9-22 P]; the announcement of the flood [7:1-5 J]; and finally, leaving the ark [8:14-19 P] and the promise of future preservation [8:20-22 J + 9:1-17 P]) while more closely interweaving both of the sources of the actual flood story itself.

The remarkable thing is that in the flood story the story lines of both source writings can be identified individually and reconstructed almost without gaps (for example, this has been done by Gerhard von Rad in his commentary) and that the story in its final form, despite several duplications and inconsistencies, comprises a meaningful whole to which our interpretation must adhere.

Despite the characteristic differences, the flood story from both sources was congruent in terms of narrative and theology, making the attempt at interpretation possible.

The following outline illustrates the complete story:

6:5-8	Introduction: God's decision to destroy humankind	J
6:9-12	Noah and the evil of all flesh	P
6:13-22	Announcement of the flood and command to build the ark	P
7:1-5	Instruction to board the ark	J
7:6-24	The flood	P: 7:6, 11, 13-16a, 17a, 18-21, 24; J: 7:7, 10, 12, 16b, 17b, 22, 23a, 23c
8:1-12	The receding of the flood	P: 8:1-2a, 3b-5; J: 8:2b, 3a, 6, 12, 13b
8:13-19	Instruction to leave the ark	P
8:20-22	Noah's offering and God's promise	J
9:1-17	End: God's covenant with Noah and all flesh	P

3. The Biblical Story of the Flood

In the following pages, I will attempt to interpret in its present form the biblical story of the flood. The differences between the two accounts will not be glossed over but will be retained with respect to the verses that are woven together.

God's Decision to Destroy Humankind (6:5-8)

Beginning the early priestly account, the passage stating the reason for Yahweh's decision to destroy humankind introduces the whole story. Many interpreters have viewed the personal theological handwriting of the Jahwist in these few verses and in the corresponding final remarks in 8:21, which has served to give the transmitted flood story its interpretive stamp. In addition, it is, quite independent from this source, an important element for the story's interpretation.[8]

The formula "and Yahweh saw" initiates the divine diagnosis regarding the condition of humanity. It is decidedly negative: "The LORD saw how great [humankind's] (here again Hebrew: *ha' adam*) wickedness on the earth had become, and that every inclination of the thoughts of [their] hearts was only evil all the time." This is more than a summary of what Genesis 3–6:4 says about the history of the problem. These are the symptoms of a basic problem that cannot be overlooked any longer: humans and what they think and do (Luther translates it congenially as their "coming and going") are determined as "evil" from within. "Without any cynicism, but in astonishing clarity, it says here with complete austerity that despite so many unending plans that were made in the name of everything good, just, or even divinely inspired and inspiring, many bad things were created."[9] The negative judgment appears to be complete: *everything* that results from human plans is *always* evil, meaning that it is ultimately not life supporting but destructive of life. However, it is undeniable that there is also goodwill among humankind and that people have a substantial amount to contribute. However, the results do not hold up to God's judgment because they always involve what is detrimental to life.

The result is astonishing: "The LORD was grieved that he had made [humans] on the earth, and his heart was filled with pain"

(v. 6). The fact that God could regret an action was something that was seen for centuries as a completely inappropriate way of talking about God. An all-seeing and all-powerful and in his way unchanging God could not regret or rue something that he had willed or done! Even the Bible appears to reject this, as it says in 1 Samuel 15:29: "He who is the Glory of Israel does not lie or change his mind; for he is not a man, that he should change his mind" (see also Num. 23:19). However, the same thing is said of God in connection to 1 Samuel 15:11: "I am grieved that I have made Saul king" (compare v. 35).[10]

Apparently, for the biblical narrative, this anthropomorphic expression is the best way to express something that is entirely unexplainable—namely, that God must condemn what he has created or those whom he has called. The fact that this is not a result of a mood but comes from a deep cleft in God's heart is shown in the parallel verse in verse 6: "And his heart was filled with pain." The same verb is also used in 2 Samuel 19:3 for David's pain regarding his son Absalom, and is hidden in the verses of Genesis 3:16 about the "hardship" of human life. God suffers the failures of humankind,[11] and thus in his judgment there is an internal tension right from the start that is only partially resolved in the parallel verses in 8:21.

The decision is final: "I will wipe humankind, whom I have created, from the face of the earth," which includes the animals as self-evident, but without further explanation. It is impressive how the story seeks to avoid any dualistic manner of speaking and expressly mentions three times that God must destroy what he has made (i.e., created)! God's good creation hides the possibility of evil, which has developed against his will, so that now, in order for God to remain true to the yes of life, he must destroy created life and in a certain sense "take back" his yes. This is an almost unbearable claim for an idea of the divine in which God's power and omnicausality are connected to a type of unbroken affecting and all-determining causality. For a theology that connects its language of God and his actions with the very much more open concept of causality in modern science, the recollection of biblical statements can be an important aid in helping gain a new perspective on God and his actions. Thus, the English biochemist and theologian Arthur Peacocke writes: "The unpredictability and openness to the future of much of what happens in the world happens especially in the sphere of free men, meaning that we find ourselves in the situation of having to say that God took a risk with creation, and that he exposed himself to vulnerability through what the developing entities in creation can and might be able to do."[12]

The Old Testament story shows something of God's openness, without diminishing the sovereignty of his actions. This is expressed by an observation that is surprising in view of the negative judgment on the consummate evil of humankind: "But Noah found favor in the eyes of the LORD" (v. 8). This contradiction is clearly not absolute, for it does not first indicate that Noah represents an exception to God's negative assessment. The early priestly writings provide no information on Noah's behavior. They say only that "Noah found favor in the eyes of the LORD," a phrase that in biblical language describes the openness of God's conditions and terms and bestows salvation and new community with him (compare Gen. 19:19; Exod. 33:12; 2 Sam. 15:25).

Why God chose Noah, and through this judgment made possible a new beginning for human history, is not stated. Contrary to the Babylonian flood story, law and grace are not divided between different divine actors but are incorporated into the heart of the one God.

Noah and the Destruction of All Flesh (6:9-12)

The mention of Noah in the early priestly writings is an occasion for the editor to shift to the perspective of the priestly writings, as they provide a more complete report of Noah and of God's plans for him. Noah's name also provides the key word for a transitional headline: "This is the account of Noah" (v. 9). Here again we translate using the multiple definition of the Hebrew word *toledot*, which actually means "procreation"—namely, "descendants"—connecting it with the term *history* (compare 2:4) since genealogy and history had a close internal connection for ancient Israel.

The perspective of the priestly writings emphasizes almost opposite accents from that of the other narrators, thus creating a type of chiastic composition. Whereas the Jahwist in 6:5-7 told of the complete depravity of human beings and God's decision to destroy them, and then briefly told of Noah and God's acceptance of him, P begins with the portrayal of the righteousness of Noah in order, against this background, to tell of the total depravity of the earth.

In today's canon, J establishes the theological omen: what is said positively about Noah lies in the fact that he found favor in the eyes of God. P shows what that has done in Noah's life. Thus, it does not have to do with a linear causal explanation or with the fact that because Noah was a righteous man with a flawless life he found grace with God. Rather, the various points of both stories show two different sides of the relationship, which is established by the fact that Noah found favor with God. The stories look at the life of Noah thus: he is a "righteous man"; in Hebrew he is a *zaddiq*. In German we translate the word as "just," which is a social concept and describes solid and loyal behavior in the community of people and before God. Parallel to this is: "He was blameless among the people of his time." The Hebrew *tammim* ("without blemish") stems from the cultic arena and determines the divinely consecrated, blameless, sacrificial animal. Noah is thus one who among his peers has kept entirely to God. This is underscored by the statement "He walked with God," a fact that is reported of Enoch in Genesis 5:22 when God took him to Godself. However, Noah remains connected to human history, so we have the subsequent reference to his three sons.

After Noah is introduced and it is clear from his example what a successful life with God looks like, the priestly writings go on to tell of judgment over humankind as a whole. This judgment is at first almost formulated as a neutral claim in order then to be repeated once more as the judgment of God. This provides the basic statement that is repeated more times and given great weight: "Now the earth was corrupt in God's sight and was full of violence. God saw how corrupt the earth had become, for all the people on earth had corrupted their ways."

Four observations should be noted regarding this statement:

(1) The Hebrew word that we translate as "corrupt" has a double meaning, as does its German equivalent. "Corrupt" means "morally reprehensible," "identified through misdeeds"; but it also means "destroyed," "rotten," and "unusable." Thus, the internal and external conditions of the earth correspond to each other.

(2) Whereas J speaks of the evil of man (*'adam*), meaning the evil of humankind, in P the evil has to do with the depravity of the earth. Here we also have a systematic perspective: the entire earth—or, as it says in the end, "all flesh"—is infested with the corruption that proceeds from humans. Indeed, in P "all flesh" can mean people only, but in the parallel verse in verse 13 the decision to destroy all flesh clearly also includes animals.

(3) In terms of content, corruption is portrayed in concrete terms. The earth is full of violence (Luther: "crime"). Violence (Hebrew: *hamas*) is everything that destroys life and devalues it. It not only has an effect on society, but also on the earth as a communal living space. "*Hamas* may well originally have meant that the misdeeds that concretely lie as a burden on the land destroy both the land and its inhabitants' relationship to God."[13]

At first glance, there are the misdeeds that humans commit. The Old Testament normally views it this way, and Westermann also argues that "all flesh" here refers to humans.[14] This may be correct with regard to the basic idea, but one should not exclude the possibility that P also intends to include the life-destroying behavior of animals as belonging under God's judgment.

(4) Many interpreters have noticed the relationship between 6:12 and 1:31. The verse "And God saw all that he had made, and it was very good" stands in opposition to the statement "God saw how corrupt the earth had become, for all the people on the earth had corrupted their ways." God's good creation is deeply damaged. P wants its readers to think that both of these statements are relatively unconnected, but they are clearly placed next to each other (P knows no story of the Fall). The inclusion of J provides the reader of early biblical history with more material for this interpretation, and yet it is still a challenge to think that the fate of those whom God has created as good are not simply allowed to come to good. In this regard, I submit the citation of a systematic theologian who, in talking about the scientific discoveries regarding the earth's development, has observed:

> When the final entities in their independence are set free, then their development as individuals . . . that is, free from God, can be allowed full reign. The basis of a world still in the process of construction conveys the element of room for play . . . and thus indirectly also conveys developments that are *not divinely willed*.

At least not everything that "nature does" must be intended by God or is "the will of God." The physical evil (destruction, deformity, catastrophe, etc.) and moral evil are the logical necessary price of a nondeterministic, openly developing, freely evolving world.[15]

Announcement of the Flood and the Command to Build the Ark (6:13-22)

The next section follows in rather seamless fashion. In verse 13 God speaks to Noah and tells him of his decision: "I am going to put an end to all people, for the earth is filled with violence because of them. I am surely going to destroy both them and the earth." This verse is a good example of what in the Old Testament is typically portrayed as noncapricious punishment; it determines and enforces what constitutes guilt in behavior and deeds. This is also the case for "acts of violence." "If the land is filled with *hamas*, then the result for its inhabitants is punishment and destruction."[16] It is indeed not incorrect when Luther, or even Westermann, translates, "The end of all flesh is decided by me"; however, the Hebrew text emphasizes much more clearly that the earth is ripe for judgment and all flesh is "at an end" (compare the formulation of the words of judgment in Amos 8:2). Verse 13b then uses a play on words once again, as in verse 11: God will destroy the earth.

But it is now clearly not the end of creation, even if it is the end of nature up to that point. God shows Noah a way to the future. In a somewhat remarkable string of verses, Noah is commanded to build an ark from cypress wood with the measurements 150 meters long, 25 meters wide, and 15 meters high and is provided with a rough building plan.

First, the reason for these measurements is given: God will allow a great flood to come over the earth and it will destroy all living beings on earth. Only Noah and his family will be rescued, with the help of the ark, and with them also pairs of all animals, including birds and "worms" (the fish are not affected by the catastrophe). God does not give Noah a reason for saving these creatures, but a brief theological explanation is provided: "But I will establish my covenant with you" (v. 18a). Here for the first time in the Old Testament we have the meaningful Hebrew word *be'rit*, which we traditionally translate as "covenant." However, in P it does not describe a mutual bond but rather the self-obligation and promise of God in favor of those with whom he "establishes his covenant."[17] The motif emerges only briefly and appears almost as an anticipation of 9:9, where, in God's covenant with Noah, a report of Noah's descendants and all living animals is given in more detail. However, this motif also sheds light on the great puzzle of the story. How can God, who just decided to pronounce judgment on humankind and the animal world, now take care that every specie—including humanity—is saved from this judgment? The implicit answer is: God remains true to Godself and to creation. God stands by his promise and makes a pact with Noah, who represents all of humanity just as God has willed it, which saves Noah and all types of living beings without having to remove the law, under which "all flesh" is rightly subject. God establishes this covenant by saving Noah, and Noah is drawn into this covenant because he hears God's saving word and obeys.

All of this does not have to do only with Noah, but also with his family, including a wife, sons, and their wives—the necessary core conditions of a new humanity, so to speak. At the same time, it has to do with all types of animals, which provide for Noah necessary nourishment, and fulfills the task of "ruling" over the animals that was assigned according to God's will.

The Babylonian flood stories (and also many of their modern copies) elaborate on the process of the building of the ark, in which discussions with neighbors and the equipping of the ark with its inventory are outlined with particular care. The biblical account, however, says in one sentence: "Noah did everything just as God commanded him." What happened is what God intended—namely, the rescue of Noah in actuality as something of a second creation event.

Instruction to Board the Ark (7:1-5)

The story now takes up the threads of J again and tells of God's invitation to Noah to board the ark, together with his whole family. Here J also offers a similar reason as P in 6:9 for exactly why Noah and his family are to be saved. However, the modern translations are missing the emphasis on the verses (Luther: "For I have found you blameless"; "For I have seen that you are righteous among men"). They give the impression that, after some kind of test, God has determined that Noah is the only righteous man of his generation. A comparison of passages such as in 1 Samuel 16:1 and 2 Kings 8:13 shows that "seeing" in verse 1b means a "learning," not in the sense of a testing but of creative selection.[18] Verse 7:1b does not contradict 6:8. The fact that Noah found favor in the eyes of God also meant that he lived his life loyal to God and true to his community. In God's eyes, Noah was the "right one" for God's work to bring about a new humanity.

In verse 2 something unusual emerges in the early priestly account. Noah was allowed to take any seven of the pure animals (or any seven pairs), whereas P speaks of only one type of pure animal from all of the types of animals (compare 6:19; 7:8). That is exactly the opposite of what we would expect in the priestly writings but is easy to explain. In the priestly writings, the cultic rules and sacrificial obligation first begin with the giving of the law on Sinai. However, the other source assumes it to be self-evident that humankind has offered sacrifices to God since the beginning of their history (compare 4:3) and only tells of Noah's sacrifice after the flood (8:20). Therefore, it may have been that among those animals appointed for sacrifice more than one pair of animals was required if life in its fullness on earth was to be preserved.

Symbolic numbers also rule the events in time in J. In seven days the great rains will begin and they will last forty days and forty nights, a number that was always used to describe a very long time according to human measurements (compare the fasting of Moses on the mountain in Exod. 24:18; 34:28; Elijah on Mount Horeb in 1 Kings 19:8; Jesus fasting in the wilderness in Matt. 4:2).

When God says at the end of his speech in verse 4b, "I will wipe from the face of the earth every living creature I have made," once more the divine dilemma is mentioned in view of the coming of judgment. The existing creatures have no existence any longer if they do not correspond to God's intention for what he has made. However, the fact that what God has made is subject to destruction at his discretion is indicative of a deep and painful contradiction.

As in P in 6:22, J concludes the report of God's command to Noah with the simple statement: "And Noah did all that the LORD commanded him" (v. 5).

The Flood (7:6-24)

In this section, the editor uses his previous technique of placing sections from his sources next to one another in larger blocks of narrative. The event of the oncoming flood makes it necessary to tell the story in a sequence, thus blending the sources more intensively with one another; or, to use a different analogy, they interlock like a zipper. This leads to a series of duplications and incongruities jammed into a small space, but at the same time it gives the story weight and drama. It is still debated as to what material belongs entirely to what source, which in turn is also not completely uniform but reflects further additions as well as where the editor intervened and filled in the gaps. Accordingly, it is helpful to trace the magnificent style of the story.

Verses 6-9 portray the entrance of Noah, his family, and all the animals into the ark. Thus, verse 6 connects to the oncoming flood with a reference to Noah's altar, and verse 10 says that after the course of seven days (the deadline named in J) the flood broke over the earth.

Verses 11-16 depict all of the events once more, but this time in more detail. For the most part, the story follows P, which, for example, includes the precise time frame in verse 11a. In addition, the portrayal of the flood in verse 11b reflects the worldview of P: the channels of the firmament open up and the flood breaks out from the heavenly ocean, and the fountains of the deep open up and the water under the earth rises up. What was carefully divided by God's creation (Gen. 1:7-10) now breaks out as chaos all over the earth.

Additionally, the narrator uses J's description: "And the rain fell on the earth forty days and forty nights." The boundless blessing of rain overtakes the earth. That is certainly the meteorological explanation of the phenomenon, in addition to which there is the cosmological one: the dams that prevent the chaos of the flood break open. The fact that God has given the waters limits is the basis for the Old Testament's trust in God (compare Pss. 33:7; 93:3; 104:6-9); that he could cease doing this appears to have been one of the early concerns of Israel.

Verses 13-16 portray once more (now with P) the entry of Noah, his family, and the animals into the ark. However, this time it is much more detailed and exact, in order not to sound pedantic. The sons of Noah are expressly named and the animals are mentioned in four categories (wild animals, domestic animals, crawling animals, and birds). It is important that "all creatures that have the breath of life" are represented by a pair and that all are rescued "according to its kind" for a new future. According to P, this all occurs on the day that the flood begins—there is little mention of the "how," since everything happened "as God had commanded Noah" in verse 16. That is enough of an explanation.

This section concludes with a very succinct remark stemming from J: "Then the LORD shut him in" (v. 16b). God himself shuts up the ark. This is an expression of his personal care, in which he seals up the group that is to be spared from the deluge. However, in so doing, he seals the division between those to be rescued and the remainder of the lost.

Their destruction is depicted in verses 17-24. First, it is told that the water swelled up and carried the ark on top of it until all of the mountaintops were covered to a depth of more than fifteen cubits (twenty feet). Then it goes on to say how the men and animals perished, "everything that had the breath of life in its nostrils." The depiction of this horrible event does not go into detail. However, since the versions of J and P are placed side-by-side, and indeed again with an account of the various genres of living creatures, the impression of the complete annihilation of all life is communicated in a very dramatic way. And once more is stressed: "Only Noah was left, and those with him in the ark" (v. 23b). The law and the rescue through the law stand opposite each other in bold relief.

The Receding of the Flood (8:1-12)

Now our attention is turned entirely to Noah and his group. How do they escape death by flood?

The report begins (following P) with a wonderful sentence: "But God remembered Noah and all the wild animals and the livestock that were with him in the ark" (8:1). Rescue by means of the ark is not accomplished automatically. It succeeds because God remembers whom he will save and for whom he cares (compare Gen. 19:29; 30:22; Exod. 22:24; Ps. 8:5). Once more it is astonishing and touching that not only Noah but also the animals are specifically mentioned. Those who have the breath of life in them are also in the community of God and in his thoughts!

God uses a series of measures to bring the flood to an end: he allows the wind to blow over the earth, making the water recede; the fountains of the deep and the windows of heaven are shut up; and (J appears here briefly) the rain stops. Accordingly, the ark settles on the mountain of Ararat after 150 days, on the seventeenth day of the seventeenth month (here the story follows the chronology of P). The geographic translation of "mountains of Ararat" is incorrect.[19] In the Bible, Ararat is the name of the land of Urartu (compare 2 Kings 19:37; Isa. 37:38; Jer. 51:27), which lies in the area of Lake Van. Much later the highest mountain in this region, towering 5,156 meters high, will be given the name Aghri Dagh, or "great Ararat." In fact, it is by far the highest mountain in the home-land of our story—but history is not interested in an exact geographical identification. The water recedes slowly, and only on the first day of the tenth month are the tops of the mountains visible.

Now the story again takes up the lines of J, which says that Noah discovers to what extent the earth is dry and inhabitable by sending out a bird. This motif is also part of the epic of Gilgamesh. Utnapishtim sends one dove out after the other, then a swallow and a raven. Noah first sends a raven, and then three times sends a dove—a procedure that the rules of the art of storytelling seldom contradict (von Rad and others will thus attribute verse 7, which mentions the raven, to P, while Westermann thinks the verse is a variation of verses 8-12).[20]

Noah must wait forty days (here again we are in a time frame of J) until he can open the windows of the ark. The procedure of gathering information by sending out a raven yields no specific information; the raven flies here and there until the water is dried up from the earth. Noah tries it with a dove, and the report of it being sent out three times belongs to the storytelling treasury of the Bible. The first time the dove comes back, apparently because it has not found a place to land yet. Noah stretches out his hand and brings it back into the protection of the ark. After another seven days, Noah releases the dove again. It comes back at evening, this time with a fresh olive branch in its beak—an image that has become a symbol of the hope of new beginnings. After another seven days, Noah releases the dove yet again, but it does not return—a sign that the earth has returned to being a place suitable for habitation.

P tries once more to assign a very exact date. On the first day of the first month in the 601st year of Noah, the waters of the earth dried up—a symbolic date for a new beginning; and on the twenty-seventh day of the second month, the time is ripe and God calls Noah and his sons out of the ark. Once again the animals are specifically mentioned by name and their meaning renewed: "so that they can multiply on the earth and be fruitful and increase in number." The earth again opens itself up as a living space for humans and animals, as God had intended in the original creation (compare 1:21). Verses 18-19 bring the complete announcement, almost with the exact words in which God's command was formulated. Life goes on again in its fullness because God wants it so and because he makes it possible.

Noah's Sacrifice and God's Promise (8:20-22)

The story of the great flood reaches its goal: with the saving of Noah and his sons, God opens up a new future for life on earth. First, the Jahwist, or J, shares his short, concentrated report of the end of the flood.

Noah builds an altar—this is the first time that this is mentioned in the early history—and makes a burnt-offering sacrifice to God of all the pure animals. In this type of sacrifice, when the animal is entirely burned up it signifies that all of the animal belongs to God.

Noah's sacrifice is one of thanksgiving. Just as Cain and Abel gave thanks for the harvest and the firstborn of the flock, so now Noah offers one of each of the pure animals as thanks for rescue from the flood. It has been asked whether this sacrifice could also assuage the wrath of God. Thus, verse 21 speaks of the "pleasing aroma," which means, literally translated, "a calming smell" or "smell of reassurance," that God smelled. This extraordinary anthropomorphic-sounding statement is at the same time a very clear play to the story contained in the Gilgamesh epic. Here also the rescued Utnapishtim brings a sacrifice to the gods after the flood; and the story goes on to say: "The gods smelled the aroma;

the gods smelled the pleasing aroma; the gods behaved like flies around the offering" (XI, 159–61). A disagreement then ensues about whether the gods, who wanted to destroy humanity, should be allowed to enjoy the expensive sacrifice! The proximity of the linguistic expression also betrays the basic difference in the interpretation between God and humankind. Neither is Yahweh dependent upon the sacrifice nor should or can his decision to exercise the law be influenced by a sacrifice. The story of the flood therefore does not speak only of the wrath of God but of his grief over the destruction of the earth (6:6). Accordingly, the traditional language about sacrifice is that of the "smell of appeasement" (compare Exod. 29:18; Lev. 1:9; and so on), an expression for God's gracious acceptance of the sacrifice as sign of reestablished community.[21]

The reference to God's covenant, which is cited in what follows, is not primarily with Noah or humankind but with the earth. The earth will not be destroyed again on account of human beings. The common fate of *'adamah* and *'adam* will no more put into question the life basis of all living things, even if humans are not up to their task "to work it and protect it." And thus the claim that "every inclination of the thoughts of their hearts was only evil all the time," which was in 6:5 cited as the basis for the decision to destroy all that lives, becomes here the basis for God not wanting to "harm" all living things or to annihilate them.

There is, however, no talk of a "curse" in 6:5-7, so many interpreters like to use 3:17 as a reference point instead. However, there is another Hebrew word for "cursed" (*'arur*). The word used in 8:21 (*qlal pi*) does not mean "cursed" in the greatest sense of the word, but rather "to defame," "make contemptible," and "to disparage."[22] It assigns a value to the living space of the earth that God no longer wants to touch, although (or even because) the activities and plans of humans continually manifest themselves as counter to life. God has not resigned himself as a result of human beings' inability to improve their behavior, but gives value to what humans corrupt—and not only to counter their corruption. Humankind remains tied to the earth, but the fate of the earth will not depend anymore on the good behavior of humankind—at least not according to the intention of God. And it is remarkable that, for the narrator, both decisions come from the innermost part of God—namely, his heart (compare 6:6 with 8:21). God does not regret his decision, since it expedited the law. Both law and mercy come from God's heart and are according to his true will. Without invalidating the law (or ascribing it to another divinity, as in the Gilgamesh epic), mercy still has the last word.

This all leads to God's celebrated covenant, which is not expressly promised to humankind but rather appears to be formulated as a crowning statement for God himself:

> As long as the earth endures,
> seedtime and harvest,
> cold and heat,
> summer and winter,
> day and night,
> will never cease.

This is not a guarantee of eternal existence for the earth. "As long as the earth endures" (literally, "all the days of the earth") indicates a limitation on the days of the earth. However, within this broad time frame there is the reliability of the rhythm of life that completes the cycle of nature: seedtime and harvest, cold and heat (which in the Orient is something similar to the fluctuation of years as well as to the hours of the day), summer and winter, day and night. Despite many fluctuations and changes in climate, summer and winter always come again, which allows for seedtime and harvest; and the reliable rhythm of day and night remains, which according to God's will should help build trust in humankind. The fact that here "a starting form of the knowledge of laws of nature" is encountered indicates the reliability and comprehensibility of the natural historical order as a gift from God.[23]

Are humans therefore relieved of their responsibility? Does this represent carte blanche for the destruction of the world and the ruin of the climate? We must think about these things if we are going to take a look at the story of the flood. Perhaps is it not by chance that these wonderful, reassuring words comprise an indirect message from the "heart of God." They are good and comforting to know, but cannot be used as a slogan or as a free license for ecological ignorance.

God's Covenant with Noah and "All Flesh" (9:1-17)

The conclusion of the flood story relies once again on the priestly writings. Here again Noah and his sons feature prominently, but—as is always the case with P—in connection to the fate of all living things.

This section has two parts:

- 9:1-7   The renewed blessing and task of creation for people, under different conditions

- 9: 8-17 God's covenant for human beings and animals, and his visible sign

In verses 1-7 the new beginning of humanity is fulfilled through God's blessing, which applies to Noah and his descendants. The task of creation is to "be fruitful and multiply and fill the earth," which is repeated again literally in 1:28. However, the way in which people will rule over the animals will now be different. It is a dominance that spreads "fear and dread" and that gives humans power over the lives of animals.

These linguistic motifs comprise the language of "holy war." The freeing of the animals is established through a relationship between humans and animals that is characterized by struggle. However, this relationship does not necessarily result in death. In the tradition where the divine action of acquiring land is spoken of in terms of "fear and dread," words used here in 9:2 (compare Deut. 2:25; 11:25), the fear and dread has to do with "the fear of God [that] falls on the enemies of Israel, and they are literally 'destroyed' so that Israel can take over their rightful land without a fight."[24] Likewise, it has to do with the undisputed dominance of humans over animals. However, death is no longer excluded. For now the animals are clearly meant as a means of nourishment for humans, whereas up until this point humans could only eat plants and their fruits. (Presumably, it was also accepted as a matter of course that the animal world was divided between herbivores and carnivores.)

A reason for this is not given. Does God sanction afterward that which before the flood had been given over to violence in his creation (compare 6:11)? The sequel in verses 4-6 speaks against this. Or is it assumed that the new humanity is no longer only vegetarian?

Genesis 9:2 states that despite the new beginning there is no simple return to preflood conditions. God's blessing continues on in the same way as the charge to populate the earth. However, from the peaceful coexistence between humans and animals under human command, competition and rivalry have developed. And in this new state of affairs humans receive priority. From "ruling over the animals" in Genesis 1:28, humans should now be the "lords of the animals."[25] Not only should the wild animals spread fear and dread—a much more dangerous reality in ancient Israel—but so should human beings, who need food. This also exists under God's blessing, but with two clear limitations. They are outlined in verse 4 and verses 5-6, in Hebrew, and otherwise only prefaced with a warning.

Verse 4 means literally, "You should not eat flesh with its life [or its soul: *nephesh*], that is, its blood." The exact meaning of this statement is not easy to figure out. On the surface, it appears that only meat that has been bled out is all right to eat, which naturally excludes the enjoyment of blood. But the structure of the Hebrew text also indicates a deeper meaning. In addition, the killing of animals is not simply yielded up to humanity's disposal. Enjoying meat is not the incorporation of life, a fact that doubtless manifested itself for ancient humans, especially with regard to the enjoyment of blood. The ancient world knew a variety of blood rites in which it was thought that the enjoyment of blood meant to experience the acquisition of the power of life. Here the Old Testament faith sees God as placing a limit that applies to all people. Despite the observance of such limits, humanity is empowered to kill animals for the purpose of food. However, these limits do not allow people to become lords over life and death. "The spilling of blood should not result in the enjoyment of blood."[26] And that has further implications for the question of how animals should be killed for *ritualistic* purposes and what flesh may be consumed: wherever there is concern over nourishment there emerges a bloodlust, drawing humans together in brutality and violence. The meaningless butchering of herds of bison on the prairies of the American West and the murderous dealings with the indigenous American populations has deep connections to this perspective.[27]

This leads to the second limitation (vv. 5-6). After the flood, human life is untouchable and stands under God's complete protection. Human life is entirely in God's hands; if a person takes another's life, God will demand the person's life in return. Thus, verse 6a is not a command to implement the death penalty, although that possibility was already the case in the Old Testament (compare for example Exod. 21:28-32 with regard to killing animals that have killed a human). The exact translation of this sentence says: "Whoever spills the blood of a man, will have his blood spilled by men. I will demand an accounting for the life of his fellow man and from every animal." This is an apodictic judgment, which at the same time harks back to an obvious experience. Matthew 26:52 is similar: "For all who draw the sword will die by the sword." How God claims the life of a murderer remains open. That this may also occur through humans, as the current translation says, and that according to the grammar would be completely feasible, remains open. Basically, however, the requirement to forfeit a life is God's business—for only thus is the reason given in 6b harmonious: "For God has made [humankind] in his image." The special relationship of human beings to God, which was a part of creation, is still in operation. It has not been lost, but is based on the unique worth of human life. The fact that humans are representatives of God is not seen here under the aspect of the power of lordship, but indicates that the life of any human stands under God's protection. This aspect of being in God's image is increasingly important for our age.

Thus, the mandate of creation is not forgotten; it is cited according to Genesis 1:28 in verse 7 as well as in verse 1, with some small variations.

In verses 8-17 the basis for the future of humankind and animals is the covenant that God establishes with them. Here it can be clearly seen that the Hebrew *be'rit* means something other than a contract that is entered into between two people. For neither Noah and his sons nor the animals are asked about, or in any way actively drawn into, the drafting of the covenant. God goes of his own accord into the service of Noah and his descendants and here again expressly includes all types of animals. He establishes his covenant—that is, he binds himself to his decision not to cause another flood over the earth that would destroy all life. God's covenant with Noah is the promise of life for all of creation.[28]

Similar to J in 8:21, where the reason for the flood refers back to 6:5, so also in P 9:11 reference is made to 6:11, giving the reason for the law of God. God will no longer corrupt "all flesh"—namely, the earth. This is an unconditional promise that does not exclude the possibility that after the flood the earth again could become "corrupt" through human fault. Nevertheless, God's promise is binding.

This is underscored in verses 12-17 through reference to a sign for God's covenant and the validity of his unbreakable promise. The rainbow, "God's bow," will be seen if the threatening clouds of anxiety awaken in light of a new flood, and will then recall God's promise. Many interpreters stress that the word *bow* does not just describe a geometric half circle that appears in the clouds but identifies it as God's bow of war.[29] The basis for this is that the Hebrew word *qäschät* always describes the hunting bow of the hunter or archer, even though here and in Ezekiel 1:28 it means the rainbow. The bow of war is a symbol of strength and lordship. Thus, the rainbow is less a symbol of mildness and patience, and more a sign of the constant lordship of God who protects against destruction from within and without. However, this is nowhere indicated by the text, so that the play on words with the bow of war certainly does not stand at the forefront of the verses.[30]

Interestingly enough, the bow also does not serve so much as a sign for humans in their hour of anxiety; it is a sign of remembrance for God himself, as verses 14-15 and verse 16 underscore with two parallel formulations. It is a sign that God recalls his duty to humankind and animals—a duty he binds in his covenant with them. It therefore serves indirectly as an affirmation of humans to remind them that God will not forget them or his promise to them. "The preservation of [humans] and the protection of life lies completely and unconditionally with God: he remembers."[31]

4. After Us the Floods Can Come— The Meaning of the Flood for Today

In recent years, the story of the flood has made a comeback. In accounts of natural catastrophes, the phrase "floodlike rains" turns up again and again. The ark and the rainbow have become cherished symbols of ecological responsibility. In the meantime, many Christians have difficulty seeing the rainbow as a biblical symbol because it appears to them to be so esoterically overloaded.

This type of reception of the story of the flood is relatively new, since it previously had an entirely different emphasis.

4.1 The Biblical and Postbiblical Reception

Similar to the paradise story, internal Old Testament allusions to the flood seldom occur. According to Ezekiel 14:14, 20, next to Daniel and Job, Noah is one of the model righteous men. This corresponds to the Noah tradition in P. Isaiah 54:9 connects with the end of the flood story (8:21; 9:11-17): "To me this is like the days of Noah, when I swore that the waters of Noah would never again cover the earth."

Many more allusions can be found in early Jewish writings (1Q Gen. Ap. 1-17; 1Q 19-20; 4Q 534; 6Q 8; 1 Hen. 106; Jub. 4:2-10).

Genesis 9:1-7 connects the rabbinic interpretation of the seven commands to Noah. This is not only intended for the Jews, but for all humans (i.e., the command to administer justice and the prohibition against fornication, murder, theft, the consumption of the flesh of living animals, and worshiping idols; compare also Apg. 15:20, 29).[32]

In the New Testament, the flood story is a model of the coming of the law (Luke 17:26; Matt. 24:37). In 1 Peter 3:20, the judgment typology is also a salvation typology: the saving of Noah and his kin through the judgment of the flood corresponds to the saving of Christians through the waters of baptism.

Without the Christian interpretation of the flood story, one can assume that the paradigm of judgment stands at the forefront.[33] However, although the flood story has almost the same weight in ancient history as the creation story, it has been given much less theological attention.

For a brief period, the story also garnered the attention of science. Scientists thought that the deposits from melting glaciers were signs of an all-encompassing flood during the Ice Age and therefore named the first phase of this period the "deluge," an expression that the older research of that time had coined for the Ice Age. In *An Essay towards a Natural History of the Earth* (1695), the

English doctor and geologist John Woodward (1665–1728) put forward the thesis that fossils were the remains of dead creatures from the flood. Until then, one had assumed they were just flukes of nature. Woodward convinced the influential Zurich doctor and natural researcher Johann Jakob Scheuchzer (1672–1733), who in his enthusiasm published an article in 1726 mistakenly stating that the skeleton of a giant salamander found in the area of Öhningen quarry was the "leg bone of a person drowned in the flood."[34]

This interpretation soon gave way to an articulated history of the earth using the remains of fossils. Georges Cuvier suggested that there were many different floods that fossil remains could identify. Only in books like John C. Whitcomb and Henry M. Morris's *The Genesis Flood,* and similar creationist works, does the flood serve as a key event for the partially astute explanation for all geological formations. They state that the fossils contained in the formations are the result of a large global catastrophe. However, in German-speaking areas during the last century, there have been—as far as I can tell—no serious attempts to make plausible the saving of the entire animal kingdom in a large crate.

Thus, by reputation and in practice the story of the flood became the model for a story about judgment that was overcome by God's goodness—albeit still with a certain warning potential—but it primarily conveys the comforting message that God stands by his promise not to destroy the earth on account of human beings.

4.2 Ecological Aspects

Here we have criticism but also a new positive emphasis from the ecological movement. For, indeed, the flood story offers biblical material stating that the earth's ecosystem is threatened with destruction on account of humanity's excesses. Connections, which over many centuries could only be seen as the result of the sovereign (or even arbitrary) judgment of God, have received new and immanent validity. Because humankind uses nature without care, the existence of many creatures is in danger. Since Rachel Carson's *Silent Spring* or the first report of the Club of Rome, which continued with scenes of an "atomic winter," or global warming's threat to the surface of the ocean, sensible people are seeing the possibility of global catastrophe as even more imminent. Global catastrophe will indeed certainly not destroy all life on earth, but will still deeply influence its current state. The hesitancy of many people—including politicians—to recognize, on the basis of this warning signal, the serious consequences, appears to come very close to a stance of "When we are gone, let the floods come."

Thus, people have begun to call for a new "Operation Noah's Ark" in order to save nature as we know it. Sometimes such undertakings are correctly portrayed in the media. For example, trying to save animals from flooding after the building of a new dam. However, something much more encompassing and integrated on many levels is needed for the global ecosystem.

Such undertakings are even in contradiction to the scope of the flood story with its comforting, calming promise that God will not destroy the earth again for the sake of humankind. Isn't the flood story counterproductive from an ecological viewpoint—a possible reason that it is not mentioned at all in the collected volumes of *Ecological Theology* by Günter Altner? Isn't there a danger that the "aroma of reassurance" of Noah's sacrifice has become a kind of anesthesia for subsequent humanity and that the rainbow signals less of an ecological sign of hope than it does the temptation not to take responsibility?

4.3 The Message of the Flood Story for Today

First, whoever today talks about the story of the flood may recall the film by Roland Emmerich titled *The Day after Tomorrow*. They may also recall that on December 26, 2004 (and also more recently) a flood catastrophe took place in the Indian Ocean, as a result of a seaquake near Sumatra. Commentators speak of the event as having "apocalyptic magnitude," thus giving it the tone of the "ancient preend times," as in the biblical tradition. In light of the sudden, almost inevitable breaking in of the devastation over clueless people, one is reminded by New Testament verse: "As it happened in the time of Noah . . ." (Luke 17:26). However, the time to build an ark is not here!

Despite its disastrous consequences, the catastrophe was still a regional event, which doubtless caused an outpouring of donations but did not have any effect on the stock exchange. Whether in retrospect a similar caesura will have an effect on human consciousness, as in the 1755 earthquake of Lisbon, is still an open question. The reconciliation of such an event appears difficult when there is no identifiable guilty party—as, for example, in the flooding on account of the deforestation of the forests, or as in the case of the effect of earthquakes on badly built and run-down houses. When the tsunami was unleashed as a result of the clashing of two tectonic plates under the bottom of the ocean, one could at most point to a faulty warning system. The flexibility of the earth's crust, which is evidenced by the tectonic plates, quite possibly even belongs to the requirements for existence of life on the earth.

For an atheist like Richard Dawkins, such events appear to fit entirely into the world picture: "The universe that we observe has precisely the qualities that one would expect if no plan, no design, no good or evil hides behind it—nothing except blind, merciless indifference."[35]

For Dawkins, there is thus also no problem of meaning with regard to a tsunami. However, for people who believe in God, there is the renewed question of theodicy. How can God allow such events? Or to ask the question in more depth: Why did God create the earth, upon which life exists and can develop but at the cost of being threatened from within and without? What answer does the story of the flood give here with its tension between the latent threat to human existence and the divine guarantee of earth's existence?

Second, the story of the flood represents the biblical interpretation of a catastrophic experience that was deeply rooted in humanity's collective consciousness. Large floods in Mesopotamia, the traces of which were discovered by Leonard Wolley during his excavation of Ur,[36] and those that were a result of underwater earthquakes or volcanic eruptions such as in the Mediterranean Sea—the last because of the eruption of the volcanic island of Thera in the sixteenth century before Christ—provided the background for the people in the ancient Orient. For Israel, it is not only evident in the flood story but also in the Psalms, where preservation in the face of a flood—and especially rescue from it—is by far the most important characteristic of God's creation-preserving and saving activity (compare Pss. 18:16; 32:6; 33:7; 46:3; 69:15; 77:17, and so on).[37] This is remarkable for a people in Mesopotamia and shows something of the archetypal power of these experiences.

Third, flood stories are stories of rescue. Behind them is the knowledge that human existence on this earth is endangered and that to survive is grace. The reason humanity is threatened by annihilation is represented very differently in the various myths. The fact that a person, or especially a human pair, is rescued and that humanity survives as a result is mainly referenced with regard to the action of one of the human-friendly divinities who overrules the other gods' decision in favor of annihilation. In the biblical account, a strong monotheistic tone is characteristic. It is the same God who establishes fallen humanity and all of life who chooses to save Noah and with him all living things, and who establishes that life on this earth should no more be extinguished. This causes considerable tension with respect to the view of God. Norbert Baumgart claims to be able to discern three types of gods, who determine the events of the Babylonian myths in various ways,[38] in the depiction of God in the story of the flood. However, the message that law as well as grace is contained in the unity of God's will marks the message of the biblical account. The logic of the double direction of God—his regret for having created a world filled with power and his decision not to destroy the earth again on account of human beings—is not solved by the attempt to try to comprehend God's decision. Above all, the step from the decision to destroy to the one to rescue Noah, and then to the "conditional guarantee for the earth," remains lacking in clear motivation. Rather, the logic develops through a grateful retrospective on the event: the Old Testament narrator does not ask whether it was reasonable for God to send a flood over all of humankind. The flood happened, and there could be no doubt that humanity, as it represents God's judgment, had brought the law down upon itself. And yet humanity still survived and multiplied all over the earth—although its power prevailed anew. Thus, one hears both things in the flood story: the warning not to step into false security, and the assurance that God's loyalty will guarantee that this earth will remain a livable space. The report of God's punishing activity is surrounded by the promise of his will for salvation and preservation. Thus, the unconditional promise of 8:22 is interpreted in terms of the current total concept that God's covenant—his self-obligation to preserve life— also includes humanity's obligation to protect life within the framework of the real possibilities offered by the earth itself (9:3-7).

Fourth, the fact that the story of the flood tells of the judgment of all of humanity also warns against the hasty news that Christianity often touted—namely, that the victims of local and regional catastrophes were somehow guilty of bringing it upon themselves and thus were being punished for it. Accordingly, this illustrates what Jesus said about the victims of the collapse of the tower in Jerusalem: "Those eighteen who died when the tower in Siloam fell on them—do you think they were more guilty than all the others living in Jerusalem? I tell you, no! But unless you repent, you too will all perish" (Luke 13:4-5). Not assigning guilt but rather having an orientation toward God in view of the latent threat to one's own existence is what is called for. The flood story does not so much stress the conversion of humankind but rather God's renewed attention to his creation in which he does not give up on his project of "humanity" even though he has exposed the fact that human beings are not "basically good" but are from their youth and at the base of their hearts "evil"—that is, hostile to life. This harsh, and in many ways perhaps also overly sharp diagnosis, stands in service of soteriology.[39] God is loyal to his creation, although the obverse is also conceivable, as paradigmatically shown by the flood itself. The warning scenario of the flood is thus not meant as a threat, but still remains as the dark background before which the colors of the rainbow brightly shine as God's guarantee for this earth.

Noah's sacrifice after the flood provides the implicit blueprint for a new relationship with God that is characterized by thankfulness, illustrating that survival is not self-evident nor should it be characterized by a "we have come out of it once more" as the order of the day. God's covenant, commemorated by his rainbow in the clouds, includes humankind's obligation to protect life. For those who are shaken by catastrophic events, this symbol also holds God's sign of his promise never to destroy the world. It is, however, also a remembrance that God's guarantee does not mean free reign to destroy creation, but is the foundation for responsible action.

Finally, the connection between creation and salvation through the judgment of the flood is constitutive for ancient biblical history. It is found in J and P and was also relayed by Babylonian models such as the Atram-hasis epic. The early Babylonian story reads: "That which is called by the divine into existence and life is the same as what is being continually preserved by the divine in existence and life."[40] In the biblical story, this certainty is firmly maintained through the unity of the creating and saving God. "What our God has created, he will also preserve, and thus both now and later his goodness will prevail."[41] This is also true in view of the power that is hostile to life and that breaks into creation. The breaking in of the flood into the order of creation is not so much punishment but rather the image for the breaking in of this power and the all-encompassing death that follows from it. God saves through the deadly threat, and from beyond it. His promise bans the primal anxiety of human beings from this threat, a promise which is also expressed in various forms today and creates in humans the possibility for renewed trust and thus also a place for life.

CHAPTER FOUR

VARIETY AND CONFUSION— THE EXPANSION (9:18–11:26)

The last story cycle leads into the expanding world of people. It begins with the story of a family (9:18-29)—a story that will have consequences for the communal life of people in the much-heralded land. The Table of Nations (Gen. 10) and the story of the building of the tower of Babel depict the coming reality of a humanity divided into many nations and states. The genealogy from Noah through Terah builds a bridge to the family of Abram, whose story (11:27-31) then continues seamlessly until Abram's calling (12:1-4a), marking the beginning of the story of the fathers and mothers of Israel.

Several modern authors take the position that the early history ends with 9:29.[1] The apparent thematic unity of the creation and flood, which were already depicted in the Atram-hasis epic, seems to suggest this. Additional compositional considerations, which are oriented on the three-part division of the *toledot* formula 1:1-2; 3:2, 4; 4:26–5:1-9, 29, are also introduced in support of this argument. In contrast, 10:1–11:26 through 10:32 and 11:10 are connected with the flood and "the fact that the Babel story has to do with humanity as a whole, whereas 11:1-9 acts as the unifying subject."[2]

In the early priestly writings, Genesis 9 and 10–11 depict the same thing as Genesis 2–3 and 4. The conflict between nations, as well as between human beings and God, and its meaning for human existence is once more played out on the level of the "people" (see Table 4).

The entire question is rendered somewhat relative by the consideration that according to the interpretation of the early priestly tradition in P there was no longer an independent written original story. God's story of humankind was thus read in relationship to the story of Israel.[3]

1. The Sons of Noah (9:18-29)

One of the characteristics of the early account is that next to the "great stories" of paradise and the flood other "short stories" appeared, partially as extensions of the genealogical passages. They are nevertheless stories of families and thus still have meaning for the larger whole. Such stories are found in 4:17-24 and also again in 9:18-29.

The present version of this story is confusing since it tells of an event that the three sons of Noah are involved in but which gives rise to consequences for the future: Canaan, one of Ham's sons, takes his father's place after his father has behaved badly (v. 25). In the introduction (v. 18) and then in the narrative itself (v. 22), Ham has already been identified as the father of Canaan and as someone who is relatively unmotivated and pedestrian.[4] Naturally, the intention here is clear: Canaan is represented as the "land of Canaan" and its inhabitants as the Canaanites. The curse on Canaan then provides the basis for the lower status of the early inhabitants of this land.[5]

This explanation also has its limitations: who does Shem represent? The Israelites are traced back to him, but since he is also the forebear of many other neighboring tribes he is otherwise not mentioned as a representative of Israel. And who does Japheth represent? The Philistines? This is often stated, but according to 10:14 the Philistines are Ham's descendants! Or are the Madai (10:2) representatives of the Persian kingdom, particularly of the Javan, who the Greeks thought were the Diadochi? What does it mean that they live in the tents of Shem (10:27)? This indicates the difficulty of extracting a purely etiological meaning from which to derive later political relationships. Therefore, let us follow the story as it was first intended, namely, as the story of a family.

In verse 18 the sons of Noah are once more introduced and it is emphasized that the entire population of the earth is descended from them. This also gives the following story its unique meaning!

In verse 19 the broad horizon is narrowed and it becomes a very intimate and rather distressing family story. Noah was—and is subsequently reported to be—a farmer and begins to build a vineyard (that is not specifically told) and to make wine from the grapes. In Israel wine is seen as God's gift (Ps. 104:15), and the note in 5:29 that Noah will comfort the people in the cares of their toil refers to the introduction of wine. However, the comforting and intoxicating effects of wine are closely related, and so Noah gets drunk and lies in a naked heap in his tent. Previous interpreters have gleefully suggested how realistic the Bible is to portray the weakness of a righteous man such as Noah; but recent exegetes argue that in the ancient Orient it was the right of the elderly to get drunk, and cite examples for this where sons are obligated to bring their besotted fathers safely home.[6] It is accurate that the story does not contain any reproach against Noah. The fact that he "was naked"—even if only hidden in his tent—may have registered at least some ambivalent feelings in ancient readers, but the real neglect occurs with Ham. Instead of discreetly drawing back or covering his father when he discovers his condition, by his speech he brings his father's condition to the attention of his brothers. The brothers conduct themselves in an exemplary fashion; they cover their father and avoid even looking at him in his unseemly condition.

Noah discovers the incident and reacts with a curse to the foolishness of his youngest son. The curse not only affects Ham but also one of his sons. For the ancient reader this is not as amazing as it is for us. Quite often a prominent son took the place of his father and vice versa (compare the replacing of Joseph by Ephraim and Manasseh in the biblical tradition), and indeed, as in the case of Canaan, for Israel considerable weight was given to the actual naming of a person. The curse over Canaan means that he will be the "servant of all servants"—that is, the lowest of the slaves. Through the words of blessing for both Shem and Japheth, the term *servant* was still used in a positive sense.

The first of these blessings is actually a doxology to Yahweh, the God of Shem (here Shem clearly stands for Israel), with the addition that Canaan will be Shem's slave. The second blessing applies to Japheth, whose descendants will live in the "tents of Shem," and Canaan will also serve him. Clearly, relationships are described in which the Canaanites come under the political domination of Israel and its related lines. At the same time, groups that stemmed from the west or the north, thus the area of Japheth, also resided in the area of Israel and its related tribes and even geographically dominated the original Canaanite indigenous population. This would correspond approximately to the relationships in place during the reigns of David and Solomon. Quite possibly, the blessings on Shem and Japheth did not originate at the same time and mirror various political relationships.[7]

However, we have already suggested that the etiological-political explanations of the story and the three curses, and especially the blessing of Noah, only partially address these issues. They also carry other signs and messages. For "the human way of seeing yields a satisfying explanation."[8]

Claus Westermann has suggested that after the disruption in the relationship between man and woman mentioned in chapter 3, and the break in the relationship between brother and brother mentioned in 4:1-16, now the relationship between father and sons (especially parents and children) is also taken up.[9]

In his drunken condition, Noah has created a vulnerability that will be austerely maintained. But when the son uses it in order to embarrass the father, the redemptive relationship between the generations is destroyed—yes, destroyed. Community exists by virtue of the respect of others, particularly toward the elderly and with deference to their weakness.

As a result of the disruption in human community, a new, until now unknown social structure comes on the scene—namely, that of slavery and lordship between "brothers."

The Old Testament is basically critical of lordship. Lordship of one person over another is mainly a reason for exploitation and oppression. Thus, most rulers are criticized for their misuse of power. However, there is also another side. In 1 Samuel 8:5 the petitioner Samuel wishes for a person "to rule us," based on the fact that this is the case with all peoples (also the Canaanites), which is in turn used against Samuel and his pursuits (8:10). Similarly, in Genesis 9:24 the fact of "being a slave" is not seen from the perspective of powerful oppression but as result of having a "slavish" or lower attitude. Therefore, people who use the weaknesses of others and belittle them will themselves be belittled and become the lowest slaves of all.

One must be very careful that these considerations do not lead to a cheap justification of slavery and oppression. A sign for this could be the already mentioned remarkable fact that the language about Shem does not praise him because he becomes the lord of Canaan, but rather praises Yahweh, the God of Shem, so that—if one takes the text entirely word for word—Canaan is characterized as the servant of Yahweh. This is not meant literally, but means that Canaan's slavery to Shem is not to be boundless and without limits.[10] This text has, by the way, given rise to some very inglorious consequences for which it was not to blame: the "Christian" representatives of apartheid justified the slavery of black Africans with it, saying that according to Genesis 10:6 the blacks were the descendants of Ham and were thus meant for slavery.

However, this misinterpretation does not change the fact that the story puts its finger on a sore point. When family and house (with Noah it was a tent) are no longer protection in hours of weakness, the relationship of trust breaks apart and the vicious cycle of servility and dominance begins.

2. The Table of Nations (10)

"Genesis 10 is one of the most important chapters in the Bible, even though it doesn't mention God," says Westermann of this biblical text, which for the simple reader of the Bible appears to be little more than a collection of unidentifiable names.[11] What led to such a conclusion?

It has already been said in 9:19 that the entire earth will be populated through the sons of Noah. The report of Noah's personal behavior was mentioned first so as to clearly indicate the influence it would have on the relationship to his descendants. Under the caption "These are the descendants of the sons of Noah," the lineage of the earth's people is represented in an overview as stemming from Noah's sons. What follows is no mere genealogy, as we find in chapter 5 or in 11:10-26. The names that are listed mainly describe people or lands, even if they are treated as individual names of persons. The term *toledot* ("descendants") shows us that the priestly writings afford the occasion for the following list of people. However, they are embellished, possibly through a corresponding list from J whose range of content is debated. Possibly the editor also worked on other material. We are not at liberty in the framework of our interpretation to go into detail about this but will try to summarize the intention of the text as a whole. That being said, we must briefly go through the list. A series of names can be identified, but others cannot be. A look at a map of the ancient world in a Bible or Bible atlas shows that behind the list in Genesis 10 there are some very concrete geographical locations (see Abb. 2).

The list is arranged in reverse order—the sons of Noah in 10:1 are named in addition to Japheth, Ham, and Shem—possibly because in 11:10 it continues on with Shem and his descendants.[12]

The narrative about Japheth is the briefest. To his group belongs the people of the north: Gomer (the Assyrians in Asia Minor), Magog (not identified), Madai (the Medes in northern Iran), Javan (the Ionians or Greeks), Tubal (the Tiberians in the north of Asia Minor), Meshech (the Moschoi in northeast or southwest Asia Minor), and Tiras (the Tyrenese in the north of Aegea or Italy). Gomer is still followed in the next generation: Ashkenaz could be the Scyths; Togarmah is a region in eastern Asia Minor; but Riphath is not identified. Even Javan, the large Greek area of settlements, is differentiated into Elishah (Cyprus), Tarshish (Tartessos in Spain), Kittim (Larnaca), and Rodanim (Rhodes). In verse 5 it casually says that these settlements populated the islands and coasts of the Mediterranean.

The list for Ham is more complex. Immediate neighbors are named as Cush (Ethiopia/ Nubia), Mizraim (Egypt), Put (possibly Libya), and Canaan. For most of those named there is a broad division into a "second generation." The names attributed to Cush lead into the Sudan (Seba), toward Hadramaut (Sabtah), and to southwestern Arabia (Sheba and Dedan).

It is very interesting—and certainly an insertion from another tradition—to note that Nimrod is also named as one of the sons of Cush. Here, contrary to the other names, an individual person is meant. He was apparently a known figure stemming from several anecdotal statements. They begin with him becoming a hero of war on earth; as Luther translates: "He was the first to be a mighty warrior on earth." This is emphasized by the statement, "He was a mighty hunter before the LORD," an expression that has remained intact up to the present. As the great reliefs on the walls of Assyrian, Babylonian, and Egyptian kings show, hunting was an attribute of kingly power, since power over people and animals was closely related. But the exegetical criticism is not explicit. A kernel of amazement is hidden in the story of these powerful people who were the first to conquer a kingdom and who built great cities, beginning with Babel, Erech, Accad, and Calneh, as well as famous cities in "the land of Shinar," which is in the south of Mesopotamia. The kingdom was then expanded to Assyria with great cities like Nineveh or Calah, which later became the cities of residence of Assyrian kings. In the midst of the peaceful coexistence of people there are warring powers and political figures as a result of the concentration of cultures in a city. The alienation of these elements is stressed—intentionally or unintentionally—when it is Shem who first names the people of Assyria and Babylonia (Arpachshad). Nimrod appears to be the prototype of a usurper whose empire has no ethnic connections.

Even for Mizraim (Egypt) there are "issues." Obviously, primarily Libya and the tribes of upper Egypt, but also the Kaftorites from Crete, are named in relationship to Egypt. From there we also have a description of the Philistines, the "sea people" of Egyptian history.[13]

There is no further mention of Put, but there is mention of Canaan. Eleven city-states are named from the area of Syrophoenicia. The names include several tribes that interestingly enough appear in Old Testament lists under the inhabitants of Canaan (Jebusites [Jerusalem], Amorites, Girgashites, and Hivites.) They are described as inhabiting a relatively small settlement, which they later extended and whose boundaries were marked by a series of cities: Sidon in the north; Gerar and Gaza in the south; and Sodom, Gomorrah, Admah, Zeboiim, and Lesha in the east.

The sons of Shem are given as Elam, Asshur, Arpachshad (Babylonia), Lud (Lydia), and Aram. With the exception of Lud, all were known to be people inhabiting the northeast area of the Fertile Crescent. The "sons" of Aram (v. 23) are unfortunately not identified. More generations are named as belonging to

Arpachshad (an exception). The names are probably taken from the Jahwist parallel to the genealogy in 11:12-13. The observation about Peleg is difficult to understand. It is possibly an allusion to 11:9, marking the spread of humanity over the earth within the genealogy of Shem. Peleg's brother Joktan is said to have thirteen "sons," and, as far as the names can be identified, they refer to places in southern Arabia in the area of Yemen and Hadramaut (here: Hazarmaveth).

All three lists end with the same final summary in verses 5, 20, and 31 (however, the Japheth text in the Hebrew in verse 5 is apparently incomplete) stating who the sons of X are according to their clans (Luther: "kind"), their languages, their lands, and their people. A fourfold identification scheme for the differentiation of humanity is also cited: the clans, thus the family connection, as the central unity of ancient society; the language as the conveyor of a common culture; the land as a common living space; and the people, namely, the nation, as the overriding unity for political-historical life.[14] The world of people is so richly articulated that the reference to the various languages and the vast geographical landscape that is sketched out already anticipates the result in 11:1-9.

Next to its portrayal of the variety of peoples, the Table of Nations in Genesis 10 describes an internal unity that comes as a result of their common lineage. This is underscored once more in the conclusion of verse 32: "These are the clans of Noah's sons, according to their lines of descent (*toledot*), within their nations. From these the nations spread out over the earth after the flood."

Accordingly, we have in the implicit meaning of the text something that makes it very special and important for the exegesis of the early account. We find in this chapter a presentation of the known world of people at that time, which above all had this to say: all of humanity is a family. Much of the juxtaposition of nations, cities, and names of people appears to us to be unsystematic. In many instances we cannot know exactly according to which principles the order was determined. The geographical divisions appear to regulate the order, but they are also not enforced consistently. In the course of the history of the origin of the text, lists of different lineages are apparently mixed together. Nevertheless, we can see that all of this information has been placed together without any positive or negative assessment—that is, as politically neutral. In addition, people who were seen as the traditional enemies of Israel are mentioned with the same rank and status. However, Israel itself still does not appear. Israel sees itself as a latecomer among the nations and still hides in the continuation of the Arpachshad (similar to Moab, Ammon, or Edom) family tree. There is also no indication of racial discrimination. The sons of Ham are an example: Cushites are representatives of black Africa, and Egyptians and Canaanites are mixed together without distinctions.

Naturally, from today's vantage point, all branches of humanity are related. However, the intention of the Old Testament text comes markedly close to the discoveries of modern genetics: all people are genetically linked, even among the various branches. From a genetic point of view, it would make complete sense if all of humanity were descended from one person—even if to speak of an "African Eve" were to be taken more symbolically than literally.[15]

The editors thus knowingly placed chapter 10 first as a positive text in contrast to 11:1-19, partially in anticipation of what would happen in 11:9.[16] The variety of people and the difference in the languages and cultures are not only to be evaluated as the fall of a homogenous original society and resulting divine punishment, but also as abundance and as part of the completion of the divine project to fill the earth. The fact that the descendants of Noah spread over the earth does not mean that they each had to have separate characters; they could also be described as "branching" organically. Thus, the text also presents a type of contrasting text to passages such as Isaiah 40:15: "Surely the nations are like a drop in a bucket; they are regarded as dust on the scales." Whereas, in view of a situation in which not God but other people appear to steer world history (as shown with drastic images and consequences), so little meaning and weight is gained from it that the variety of people who settled all sorts of islands and shores is seen as unfolding from the God-given fullness of blessing (compare 9:1 with 10:32). The God of Noah and his sons is also the God of the people (that is, in the language of later translations, the God of the "heathen" in Romans 3:29).

"The essential unity of the human race in all its variety" is a fact that lies in the unity of the creating activity of the *one* God. It is very well known that the story of the election of Israel is placed at the forefront: "In Genesis it has to do with a creator God and his people in the midst of a variety of divinely willed cultures and nationalities."[17] When Frank Crüsemann continues, "This also belongs to the relationship to this creator God, as well as to the other religions," then he is saying more than the text states, which noticeably factors out this theme. For the original biblical account, the variety of gods and religions existing together at the time is clearly not a theme.

3. The Building of the Tower of Babel (11:1-9)

In the story of the building of the tower of Babel we come to the last of the "great stories" of the early history. We call it "great" this time not so much because of its scope but because of its significance and the history of its consequences.

The story is arranged according to that of the early priestly writings. Although the motif of building a tower doubtless comes out of Mesopotamia, there is no direct parallel to this story in the oral history of Mesopotamia. A negative assessment of this event could only have come from the outside. Comparable elements to the individual motifs in the story can certainly be found in Mesopotamia, as well as in the lore of other ancient cultures.[18]

Although at first glance the story appears to be told in a clear and logical fashion, interpreters have uncovered various differentiated strands and story lines. Primarily, the juxtaposition of the building of a city and a tower and the intention to make a name, and the various consequences of the confusion of languages (building ceases and the people are dispersed all over the earth), has led to various reconstructions of the early history of the text.[19]

More recent exegesis has revealed that the current text represents a meaningful and very meticulously built whole, which is precisely structured through the concentrated correspondence of motifs of the action of people in verses 1-4 on the one hand, and the reaction of God in verses 6-9 on the other hand. In the center of the text is verse 5, where God perceives the strivings of humankind.[20]

The story begins with a general announcement (v. 1): "Now the whole world had one language [literally, 'lip'] and one speech."

Thus, not only was the articulation of the words the same, but also the use of the words and concepts were understandable and therefore were used to mean the same thing. Verse 2 goes on: as people steadily evolve they need a new place to live, and thus look to the east and find level land in Shinar (the southern part of Mesopotamia, which is viewed as one of the cradles of human culture). In verse 3 the culture begins with the discovery of a new method of building that allows large buildings to be erected in the marshy area of Mesopotamia, where there are no rocks. Bricks are formed, burned, and glued together with asphalt (Luther: "bitumen"). People tackle new challenges and manage them so that not only are the necessities of daily life overcome (thus accommodations or stalls are built), but also great buildings are created, which extend well beyond their immediate needs, thus constituting a culture.

Thus, humankind resolved to build a city and in it a high temple tower whose top would reach to the sky. The reasons are surprising: the people want to make a name for themselves and want to prevent being spread out all over the earth. On the one hand, the intention to build a tower whose top reaches to the sky is based on religious hubris. On the other hand, the intention "to make a name for ourselves" and to be the center of the earth's population belongs to the political realm.

There can be no doubt that our story is critical of the phenomenon of the Babylonian temple tower, the so-called ziggurat, whose construction was characteristic of Assyrian and Babylonian cities. Originally, temples were erected on the ziggurat's heights as a surrogate for mountain sanctuaries, and newer Babylonian inscriptions speak of such a tower that was built by divine order so as "to have a peak to compete with the heavens."[21] The immediate model for these stories was the Babylonian temple tower Etemenanki ("house that is the fundament of heaven and earth"), which was first built under Nebuchadnezzar I (1125–1104 B.C.), destroyed several times, and built for the last time by Nebuchadnezzar II (605–562 B.C.). With its height of ninety-one meters it was for the ancient world an unsurpassed building: the fact that for most of its existence it stood destroyed or appeared incomplete could be the reason for such a story (see Abb. 3).[22]

However, the historical tower in Babylon was only the external impetus for telling such a story, and it is significant that there was no disagreement among the cultic divinities represented in the construction.

Biblical tradition can only see in the attempt to build such a high tower—and what religious goal was to be subjectively served by such an undertaking—humanity's attempt to raise itself to the skies. In the prophetic tradition, the tendency to hubris is also connected with Babel. In Isaiah 14:13-14 there is a lament concerning Babel and the fall of the world's rulers:

> You said in your heart,
>   "I will ascend to heaven;
> I will raise my throne above the stars of God;
>   I will sit enthroned on the mount of the assembly
> on the utmost heights of the sacred mountain.
>   I will ascend above the tops of the clouds,
> I will make myself like the Most High."

Climbing to the heavens is motivated by wanting to put oneself in God's place—that is, wanting to be like God—and in this story that want is seduced by the technical possibility that was then available to humans.

However, just as in Isaiah 14, there are indications of political motives. The name Babel is a symbol of lordship, a sign of dominance and oppression. "A common name creates a supra-I, to which one can bow and subject oneself, right up to the standardizing of language in the military command."[23] The in and of itself positive-sounding motif to "not be scattered" is at the very least ambiguous, if not negative. It stands less under the sign of helpful solidarity and more under the sign of securing the power of an imperial center that allows for no global development and diversification.[24] The command to "multiply and fill the earth," which presumes differences in cultural developments, cannot be fulfilled in that case.

God reacts to this event (v. 5), something that is portrayed somewhat humorously. God must first come down to view the city and tower! Even now, the towers of human beings do not reach the heavens!

Nevertheless, God sees danger in the tower of humanity. The overstepping of the boundary of "above" in an attempt to reach the "heavens"—the sphere of God—is only the beginning of what people who are in agreement on their goal, and who can and will violate other boundaries, can accomplish once they set their minds to it. In God's words, the problem that "then nothing they plan to do will be impossible for them" has in the Hebrew text strong reference to a claim encountered in Job 42:2 with respect to God: "I know that you can do all things; no plan of yours can be thwarted." In this way, the almighty power of God is described and the danger for humans consists in giving in to their delusions of grandeur that they can do anything. The problem does not lie in that God cannot deny people anything in the future (this is suggested in the Luther translation) and must be careful to guard his supremacy because his unique divinity is in danger. It is quite the opposite: if people are denied nothing, then humanity is in danger. Thus, not only the tower that reaches up to the sky is an expression of a totality without God; the centralized and unified state is also something that threatens the humanity of humankind.

The action continues (v. 7). God places his "Come, let us . . ." in opposition to the human "Come, let us . . ." of verse 3. The situation is very similar to 3:22, where God places a limitation on human ability so that it cannot become boundless. Here God speaks in the plural in order to give weight to his words. The fact that God "comes down" (specifically, "came down") to speak shows the level of distance and alienation that has come between God and humanity. The goal of God's intervention is to confuse the language of humans so that they will not understand one another.

This is a paradoxical plan: language is there for people to be able to understand one another. On one hand, the variety of languages prevents understanding. On the other hand, a standardized unified language oppresses. Differentiation of language is necessary to accommodate the rich variety of life, and in this way it is possible to comprehend the variety of languages as described in Genesis 10. Accordingly, here is where the ambivalence lies: "The variety of the people depicts not only the variety of the creating power of God, but also a law; for the wildness of the world of people, which our story depicts as the sad end result, was not willed by God, but is a punishment for sinful rebellion against God."[25]

The story does not tell how God confuses language. It is simply stated that the people can no longer make themselves understood and that this divided them so that they could no longer pursue their lofty goals. However, this has led to the fact that those who are now spread out all across distant lands are also ultimately, and according to God's intention, spread out all over the earth.[26]

Only at the end of the story do we find out the name of the city, "Babel," and with the help of a folk etymology a connection between the name and the Hebrew verb *balal* ("confusion") is established. This large city is the place of confusion because it wants to takes God's place.

It is clear that what transpires in the story of the building of the tower of Babel is a variation of the story of paradise. The attempt "to be like God" and to overstep human limitations now emerges in a new form. It is not the possibilities hidden in God's creation that demand a limit from human grasp; rather the technical and cultural capabilities of people now need to be guarded from mis-use by humans. Strictly speaking, the confusion of language that God has caused is not a punishment but a precautionary measure that hinders people from establishing their "name"—namely, their autonomous dominion.

Today's questions apply here. Isn't there danger in this story of disparaging or of even demonizing the achievements of human technology and culture? We marvel today at the achievements of the builders who constructed the Babylonian ziggurat or the Egyptian pyramids. Perhaps we sometimes underestimate the price that some had to pay so that others could make a "name" for themselves. However, the current time is full of examples in which Christians have fought against progress because they thought that this or that technological achievement amounted to the same thing as the tower of Babel, only under other auspices. One of the more recent examples of this is the case of manned space travel, which shows very clearly how differently the broadening of horizons is handled. The Soviet cosmonauts made a point of saying that they did not encounter God on their trip into space. However, the American Neil Armstrong, the first man to put his foot on the moon, read from Genesis 1 on his return trip to earth. The reading of a biblical text does not, of course, guarantee that people are not capable of deluding themselves into thinking that this or that technical achievement is not beyond their grasp! Today we have already achieved much-hoped-for results in genome research, which continues to inspire powerful fantasies. It has also led to a clash between the beneficial uses of these advances and the desire to feel like lords over life and death, for whom "nothing is denied anymore."

Not least, the story raises the question for us today of the motivation for and price of striving for "unity." Among evangelical Christians there exists an almost neurotic fear of a unified society (and thus also of a "unified church" or "unified religion" of ecumenism). In addition, today we also are aware of a dangerous fascination with political and cultural unity, which very easily takes on totalitarian traits in connection with advanced technology. Examples for this are plentiful enough in recent memory, as well as with regard to the connection between totalitarian regimes and pseudoreligious motifs—even where atheism is the official order of the day. The fact that in Revelation 13 and 17 the term "Babylon" is used to denote the totalitarian universal power of the end times constitutes an internal biblical relationship (between the Babylon of Genesis and that of Revelation).

4. The Conclusion of the Early History (11:10-26)

Genesis 11 once more very impressively highlights the difference between both of the story lines that have been woven into the original biblical account.

The early priestly source continually names the "hot spots" that indicate problem zones for human existence and that are already very conspicuous in the story of the early beginnings. The violation of boundaries endangers the relationship between people and God, and also between their neighbors and their environment. The story of the Fall and the building of the tower of Babel shows how humans cannot tolerate the God-given limits of their existence or living on the earth in the area that is appointed to them but continually want to find salvation in and define their existence by knowing everything and being able to do everything. Both stories contain a certain ambiguity because in the "transgression"—that is, in the overstepping of prescribed boundaries—there is also something of the "transcendence" of human existence; namely, the possibility of humans overstepping their own limitations. However, both stories also show that in the damage to their relationship with God, discord erupts in the community of humans, as, for example, between man and wife according to Genesis 3, or between various cultures and languages as in Genesis 11. This break in interpersonal relationships can also be seen in Genesis 4 and Genesis 9:22. The event of the success of the brothers and the weakness of the father fails so completely in the first scenario that it results in fratricide. And in the midst of this example there is the puzzling story of the overreaching of the sons of God—of the emergence of a fascination, which at the same time still presents a dangerous relativizing of the boundaries between the human and the divine. And then there is the "yes" of the story of the flood with its interweaving of law and grace. Thus, human history reveals itself as a story of threats and failures, but also one of preservation and continuation.

In contrast to the portrayal in the priestly writings, here the continuity of God's divine creating activity and blessing is the main emphasis. The creation of the world in seven days, the descendants from Adam to Noah, the Table of Nations with its richness of human life on earth—all are an expression of the continuing effect of God's creative blessing. P also knows something of the corruption of human existence (compare 6:9), but the continuity that God creates remains in the foreground.

Thus, in the following section we have the line of descendants from Shem to Terah (especially Abram). In style and structure the genealogical list most nearly approximates Genesis 5. The schema of name, age until the conception of the first son, the remaining number of years, and mention of further sons and daughters is strictly carried through without any variation. Again, in the transmission, three different systems for the enumeration of years (MT, Sam., LXX) are used.[27] The culmination of the life span goes back continually from generation to generation, from 600 years with Shem to 156 years with Nahor; in the Masoretic text the conceptual age (except for Shem and Terah) sinks from 35 to 29 years. Only at the end is there a small variation of the schema, as was also the case in 5:32: at the age of seventy years it is said that Terah begot Abram, Nahor, and Haran, which certainly does not mean that they were triplets, but that now, instead of the continuity of generations, the fate of one generation will be followed more closely.

If the list from Adam to Noah includes ten generations, then the one from Shem to Terah only makes nine; Abram represents the tenth. His person, however, does not mark the end of an epoch, but the beginning of a new one: the story of God and the fathers and mothers of Israel.

5. The Transition to the History of the People of Israel (11:27–12:4a)

The ancient biblical account is remarkably free of allusions to the future history of Israel and the path it is to take. However, by contrast, individual story traditions appear very seldom, if at all, within the traditional narrative of the Old Testament, especially those involving the development of the people of God.

Nevertheless, the early history is not an isolated piece of tradition that one can place chronologically prior to that of the genuine Israelite tradition without having to make any connection between the traditions.

Rather, there are clear connections between them, and the section 11:27–12:4a is the fulcrum of this connection. Leading the genealogy is 11:27-31, which runs from Adam beyond Noah and Shem to Terah and continues on to Abram, the father of Israel, illustrating the particular familial relationships of the tribes and preparing the motif for the exodus from the homeland. Then 12:1-3 combines the promise of God to make a "great people" from Abram with the promise of blessing and the selection of Abram to be the bearer of that blessing. The fact that God calls an individual, blesses him, and makes him a blessing constitutes God's blessing for the benefit of all people of the earth. Thus, the motif of blessing is taken up in an entirely new way, in which the election of Israel stands in the service of blessing for all humankind.

The question is still disputed as to whether the close connection between the two traditions also applies to the nonpriestly sources. For Gerhard von Rad and—in line with his view—Hans Walter Wolff, the "disaster" of the Jahwhist's early story found its divinely willed turning point in the calling of Abram as the bearer of blessing for all of humanity.[28]

Recently, several arguments have been raised against this interpretation. One has indicated that between the original Jahwist history and the Jahwist account of pre- and early Israel in the Pentateuch there are not any connections with regard to content and that very different theological concepts can be observed in the two accounts if one is freed from having to force them together. According to the opinion of this interpreter, the stories were connected only later on, perhaps with the inclusion of Genesis into the outline of the priestly writings.[29]

To answer these questions would require a much closer investigation into the texts, something we cannot do here. Nevertheless, it is certain that the very weight of the content that was developed in Genesis 2:11 (particularly 12) is much more extensive than what the classical redactionists initially assumed about the sources of the Pentateuch. There are, however, connecting points between the Jahwist early history and 12:1-3. The motif of the "name" in 11:4 and 12:2 is such a connecting point; likewise the emerging of the term '*adamah* (earth bottom) in 12:3.[30] The curse, which lay over the earth since 3:17, has through Abram's blessed existence been transformed into a blessing for all peoples of the earth.

There is an even closer connection between the original story and the story of Abram on the level of end redaction, namely, with the inclusion of the priestly writings. The motif of blessing that is introduced in the original story of P and is conferred on all that lives is now concentrated on the elect, as designated by God's blessing.[31] This close overlap conveys universality. Abram represents the future people of God upon whom God binds his blessing—indeed, from the very beginning—with the goal that through this blessing he will bless all the peoples of the earth. Here lies the connecting point between the early history of humanity and the salvation history of God for humankind through the call of Abram, namely, Israel.

CONCLUSION

"Why must the universe undergo all of the adversity of existence?" asks Stephen Hawking at the end of his book *A Brief History of Time*,[1] thus giving the old metaphysical question "Why is there something and not rather nothing?" a dramatic new twist. The origins and history of the universe are not simply the stuff of creative potential that were seeded into the singular nature of its beginnings, but consist of struggle and suffering, evolving and decaying, emerging and dying.

The authors of the early biblical history did not ask these questions. Yet they were very aware of their environment and the myths of their time, in which the development of the world was presented as the product of the fight of the gods for dominance.[2] Against this background they formulated the stories that are collected in Genesis 1–3 and placed them in connection with the story of the origins of humankind (Gen. 4–11). What message do we want to take away from all of this?

1. The Message of the Ancient Narrative for Its Time

Basically, it is conceivable that the stories of Genesis 1–2:3 and 2:4–3:24 were first passed down like any other autonomous creation story. They are able to stand alone without a sequel. However, they were clearly included very early on in a larger narrative context—one that also contained reports of the further history of humankind and, as the second point of emphasis, the story of the flood. As the Atram-hasis myth shows, there were preoriental models for this. These common basic structures then made possible the interweaving of story lines from both the early

137

priestly original story (especially the Jahwist) and the priestly writings. Thus, the various views and theological perspectives of both stories were worked in together. However, before we attempt to characterize the results of this interweaving, let us once more bring up-to-date the message that both source writings wanted to convey.

(a) At the center of the early priestly account we see humans placed in relation to God and in relation to their fellow creatures. Humans are called to be active agents and protecting coworkers in God's creation. The story of the Garden of Eden shows that God has basically placed everything at humankind's disposal and has given them the power to make decisions over good and evil, particularly over life and death. Precisely, this leads human beings to take matters into their own hands and to try to put themselves in the place of God. Thus, a decisive break erupts in the existence of humanity. This break causes a deep alienation in relation to the Creator as well as to creation, an alienation that determines human existence from its beginnings and is thus extremely painful because it has not completely lost the remembrance of—and longing for—the original unbroken community. In addition, on "this side of Eden," an existence characterized by the fight for survival, humanity develops an abundance of cultural and technical capabilities that help it master this challenge. The decline of existence and the increase of existence thus go hand in hand.[3]

Over and over again it is demonstrated that people find it hard to live within the limits of being human. This is evidenced by their envy of the success and recognition of others and by their reaction to frustration, often with life-damaging aggressiveness and overpowering violence (Gen. 4). It reveals itself when people are open to the advances and promises of charismatic leaders (6:1-4), but also when they revel in sheer authority (9:20-27) or when they attempt to achieve reputation and power in an effort to climb to heaven with the help of technical achievements (11:1-9). All these are symptoms of a basic problem of which the radical diagnosis in 6:5 and 8:21 is: "The intentions of the human heart are only evil." In other words, what people construct and conceive is not friendly to life!

Why God's creation developed in such a problematic way is not treated as a theme. At any rate, neither an evil power nor a rival divinity is blamed for it. It is humans themselves who have abused the freedom that God has given them and who, in the attempt to control everything about their lives, fail to find life's actual meaning. What humanity now experiences as self-chosen freedom is "'purchased' at the cost of the disruption in an original childlike nearness to the Creator and is inexorably connected with the sad finality of a man freed to pursue his own enlightenment."[4]

This skeptical view of humankind's ability to positively influence the world does not mean that God will write off human beings. The impertinence to try to rule sin (4:7) also occurs after the Fall; and the possibility that humans can find grace before God and thus be found righteous before God (6:8; 7:1) provides a new beginning at decisive junctures. However, God must continually set new limits for humankind, and thus the great story of the judgment of the flood makes clear once and for all God's "no" to human evil. At the same time, the operation of the ark shows that in rescuing Noah, his family, and all types of animals God's "yes" to his creation is still immutable despite the transgressions of humans. This is made clear and concise for all time in 8:21-22—and if the early priestly history had had an earlier, shorter version, then doubtless 8:22 would have provided an impressive conclusion.[5]

However, the story does not end at this point. There is no original happy ending to the story; the problems continue in view of the relationship between generations, the origins of lords and slaves, and the attempt at a concentration of state and cultural power. Accordingly, the early history leads into the early story of humanity and ends where the history of Israel begins with the call of Abram.

We do not know what time or what particular situations these early versions of history addressed. Yet there were many parts in Israel's history in which it was important to hear this message: the fate of humankind is not the result of fighting between the gods but mirrors a basic tension between God's constant "yes" to his creation and, on the one hand, the empowering and commissioning of humans to be God's coworkers and, on the other hand, the self-empowered life that humans are able to choose through their God-given freedom whereby they continually misuse God's assignment for them, risking their own humanity.

(b) In the center of the early priestly account are God and his creating and ordering activity in the world. The creation of the world within a firm time line and in clearly defined deeds, the interweaving of creating and dividing in the process of the world's development, and the continuity of generations and the expanse of the world of people who fill the world according to God's will are all expressions of the sovereignty and reliability of God. Even the catastrophe of the judgment, which breaks into creation in the form of a flood, runs with great precision according to a clearly ordained plan. The eruption of power in God's good creation by which the earth and all creatures are destroyed is a fate that meets both people and animals. Clearly, all actively participate in it (6:13), and yet the actual cause of evil remains in the dark; it is both guilt and doom.

Although human beings are inseparably linked with all of the evil that happens on earth and are affected by God's judgment, God's assignment and blessing for them remains constant. As God's likeness humans are representatives of God's "yes" to life on earth. After Adam there were people who "walked with God" (5:22; 6:9), meaning they lived in immediate communion with God. One, Enoch, was taken up from a world corrupted by power. Another, Noah, became the rescuer who, as God's servant, brings humanity and the animal world safely through the judgment. The report of the flood remains a decisive "monument" for God to say no to power and sacrilege. However, it also comprises the dark backdrop against which God pledges his "yes" to his creation through the binding covenant of his promise. Humanity's mandate to exercise life-serving lordship over the animals is likewise renewed in the command to "be fruitful and multiply and fill the earth" (9:1; compare 1:28). Clearly, under the given conditions, the peaceful reign of humanity is "transformed to a lordship on the basis of fear and dread" (9:2).[6] However, its goal is the protection of life, and this covenant applies to both people and animals (9:3): "Everything that lives and moves will be food for you."[7]

It is interesting to note that there has never been an independent early history of P. Whatever is said here about the relationship of God to the world and to humankind is the basis for what is said of Israel's own path with its God. The covenant with Noah and his descendants is followed by the covenant with Abraham and his descendants (17:6-7) and is connected with the promise to be the father of many people. P sees the goal of this path as God's presence in the salvation on Sinai (Exod. 24:15-17), where the creating intent of God to have community with humans becomes an actuality for Israel, marking the beginning of the "change of the world into the concrete space in which to experience God's nearness."[8]

Yet what is told in the early history carries its own weight. For the Jewish people who lived in the postexilic period in the small province of Judah or in the Babylonian diaspora, it opened up a broad horizon. The fact that the God of Israel was the creator of heaven and earth was not only proclaimed but also thoroughly explained and declared. This God had given humanity its place and accompanied it through the earliest generations. He had called humanity as a whole as his regent and given it this role even after the flood. Power and guilt were original phenomena of human history—not wanted by God and avenged by him with sanctions—and still his "yes" to creation and his blessing for humanity remains in effect. And even if Israel had not appeared in the beginnings of human history, its roots were still hidden in the generations of the early times and it was this God who held them in his hands.

(c) The biblical early history as a whole is witness to Israel's faith in God's original and unbreakable "yes" to his creation. The various perspectives and highlights of both early accounts are connected to one another in a tension-filled relationship. Many aspects complement one another, whereas others appear to contradict one another and have been interpreted accordingly. We can only mention here the most important ones.

- God's "yes" to creation is the basis for all being. It is a "yes" to life in all of its fullness. It is thus also a "yes" to the existence of human beings as creatures who have a particular relationship to God.
- The world is a cosmos that was created and ordered by God, a world that was created step-by-step in which humans have an important function (Gen. 1). At the same time, humans experience the earth as their "environment" and as a God-given world of life and work (Gen. 2).

- Humankind is destined, in God's likeness, to be his representatives on earth. If, on the one hand, this role of lordship is connected with the charge to "fill" the earth (Gen. 1:28), then it is also connected to the charge to "work it and take care of it" (Gen. 2:15).
- God's determination that humans should be in his likeness stands in opposition to the attempt "to be like God" in Genesis 3. Outlining the difference between these is the core task of biblical anthropology and soteriology, and leads to the New Testament description of Christ as the true image of God (compare Phil. 2:6-11; 2 Cor. 4:4; Col. 1:15; 3:10; Heb. 1:3).
- Whatever emerges in the story of the early beginnings of humanity regarding the difficulties of life—the reduction of and threat to life—does not conform to God's original will for creation. In P, the brief mention of corruption in God's good creation is now made real through the event of the Fall, Cain's fratricide, Lamech's song of revenge, the violations of the sons of God, and, later on, through the stories of Ham's sacrilege and the building of the tower of Babel. As much as humans experience power and suffering as disasters that come over them, they must also be that much more aware of their responsibility. Evil is not connected to the effects of an ill-willed divinity; the fact that its origin can be explained at all comes from the freedom, afforded by God in his creation, that allows it to exist.
- God's "no" to evil and power manifests itself in the eruption of the flood. Both flood stories reflect, albeit from the perspective of hindsight, the overcoming of the cycle of the threat of death that springs from a life without—or in rebellion toward—God. They gratefully tell of the rescue that God gives with the help of Noah and his obedience. And both agree, although in different ways, on God's covenant to continue to protect life and the earth, despite the event of a break in his creation. Precisely because of this agreement, the flood story is the actual high point of the early history; it tells of God's constant promise to

preserve his creation despite continual new threats that destructive powers level against creation.

- People are also included in this perspective of hope. They belong to God's story of humanity—each one in his or her place. The space and time of human existence—the fullness of nations and the continuity of generations—lies in God's hands. Thus, one must not speak of nature or the gods of the people as the thrones of divine power. Creation is "divine" only to the extent that it reflects God's wisdom and goodness.

- It is not by chance that the motif of blessing threads through the early accounts. God has created this world to be a place of blessing and fullness of life. He renews this promise after the flood. Thus, the motif of blessing is also a binding element of early salvation history (12:1-4). What is often hidden *sub contrario* (i.e., under the sign of its opposite) in the events of nature and in the history of humankind can be understood as revealed through Abraham, the bearer of blessing, and his descendants.

Thus, since the postexilic period, people have read the early history with grateful astonishment at God's greatness and goodness, and with salutary fear in light of the threat to human existence. How, then, should we read it today?

2. The Message of the Ancient Narrative for Today

Today's readers have very different questions about the ancient story in comparison to those that were asked by the people of that time. Just as there were disagreements then with the tenets of ancient oriental myths about creation and their theological interpretations, so also today there are the confrontations with the results of scientific research, which are clearly, and with ever more precision and ever deeper gripping practical and theoretical implications, able to explain the origin and "function" of the cosmos and of life. However, on an existential level, there are quite possibly more points of intersection than one might see at first glance. If at that time people asked themselves whether the world and humanity were the result of a game based on the mood, needs, and arguments of the gods, then today people ask whether the universe and life are not products of a soulless evolution whereby selection is not only the guiding principle of the origin of species but is also seen as the determining force for the social coexistence of human beings.

Jan Assmann has shown that ancient polytheism was fundamentally cosmotheism; namely, the veneration of the powers that are revealed in nature and in the life of humankind and that determine the course of the world—even in their antagonistic relationships. Doubtless cosmotheism exists today in the attempt to find in the powers of the cosmos the final reason for one's own existence and for the development of all things. This takes various forms: there are scientifically influenced reasons for an esoteric pantheism that is close to ancient polytheism.[9] There are also agnostic or atheistic forms of a modern nature religion that Kenneth R. Miller has characterized in the phrase "the gods of disbelief."[10]

What science can contribute to the question of meaning is debated. Paul Davies is convinced that "science offers just as sure a way to God as religion" and that through it, inasmuch as we try to understand the world in all of its aspects, one day we will also understand "ourselves and the meaning that lies behind this universe in which we are at home."[11] However, Steven Weinberg states at the end of his book *The First Three Minutes* this often-cited sentence: "The more the universe seems to make sense to us, the more it appears to be meaningless."[12]

The answer of the early biblical account to the polytheistic cosmotheism of its time was a story of creation and early human history, which was influenced by a dynamic monotheism. Creator and creation—God and cosmos—are clearly distinguished. God continually stands alongside this world and humankind. However, he is not a "watchmaker" who finished his work in six days and now allows it to run by itself according to mechanical laws. God gives his creatures the freedom to develop and even to violate the meaning of their lives: he corrects them, suffers alongside and guides them, reacts to their deeds, and keeps his promise to creation and his creatures.

The answer of the early biblical story to the various cosmotheisms of our time could provide a clue to the ultimate reality that lies behind everything and works in everything—in what we observe in becoming and dying, and in existence and life in this world. This final reality is a personal encounter that includes everything in its immeasurable generosity and invites every person into relationship. God distinguishes himself from his creation. Nature is not God; it is a world and thus also an environment for humans placed at their disposal with the proviso "to work it and to protect it." It is place of freedom in which to continually discover new possibilities, but it also puts clear boundaries on human efforts.[13] Nature is thus not "robbed of its divinity"; it remains God's good creation where people are entrusted with responsible power as God's "regents."

God is the secret of the world, its origin and its history—a secret that continually is revealed in the unveiling of creation's bounty in the processes and the beauty of nature, but also one that is hidden behind all that is inconceivable in this world. God is a secret that is revealed for the Christian who has faith in Jesus Christ and in the workings of the Holy Spirit, and his final revelation is the hope of believing in people as the salvation of creation.

The ancient account of human existence and history is thus set against the relationship between God and his creation. It therefore makes statements about the essence and meaning of what it is to be human, which are also important today. It sees humans

- as God's beloved counterparts in the midst of a nature that is affirmed by God;
- as commissioned by God in the world, which has no meaning in itself except that in "God's likeness" humans can experience and live God's intentions ("the mind of God");
- as highly gifted by God, enabled and empowered by God as cocreating creatures of earth;
- as threatened and conflicted in their own being, alienated from God and their world; people who want to be like God and thus continually overstep the protective boundaries; people who are not hampered by technical progress but are hampered on the basis of the false premises by which they strive and work for their definition of progress;
- as bearers of God's mandate, charged with the tasks of including themselves and their cocreatures in a new

living space and maintaining culture and technology as God's gift—but always in the right balance of building and preserving culture and nature;

- as people among people; dependent upon others; bound up in the chain of generations; challenged by work and cares, envy and desires, aggression and striving for power; and called to a common enterprise that esteems life and honors its Creator;
- as creatures who live entirely by virtue of God's constancy—and who know this and make it the basis for their lives;
- as blessed by God and who, with the rest of creation, stand under the promise of God that God says yes to life and continually gives it new fullness.

This view of being human before God is also basic and guiding for us today. It invites us to encounter a God to whom not only early history but also the entire Bible bears witness. This is the God whose constancy to creation also includes a "yes" to the human creature and for whom human beings remain important despite their failures. This is the God who also blesses the unsuccessful and is true to the socially undesirable (8:21). It is—as Paul says—the God who "calls into being that which is not," who "justifies the wicked," and who "gives life to the dead" (Rom. 4:5, 17).

Table I. The Structure of the First Creation Account

Word	Deed
1. And God said: "Let there be light," and there was light. Day 1	God divides day and night and names day and night.
2. And God said: "Let there be a firmament." Day 2	God divides sky and earth and names them.
3. And God said: "Let there be seas." And it was so.	God names the sea.
4. And God said: "Let the earth be formed." And it was so. And the earth was formed. Day 3	God forms the earth.
5. And God said: "Let there be lights." And it was so. Day 4	God makes two lights and places them in the firmament
6. And God said: "Let there be fishes." Day 5	God creates large fishes and blesses them.
7. And God said: "Let the earth bring forth." And it was so.	God makes the animals of the field.
8. And God said: "Let us make humankind." And it was so. Day 6	God makes humans; God creates and blesses them.
9. And so God completed his work on the seventh day and rested on the seventh day. He rested from all his works, which he had created.	God blesses the seventh day and makes it holy.

Table II. The Story of Paradise (Gen. 2:4b–3:24) (according to Jörg Barthel)

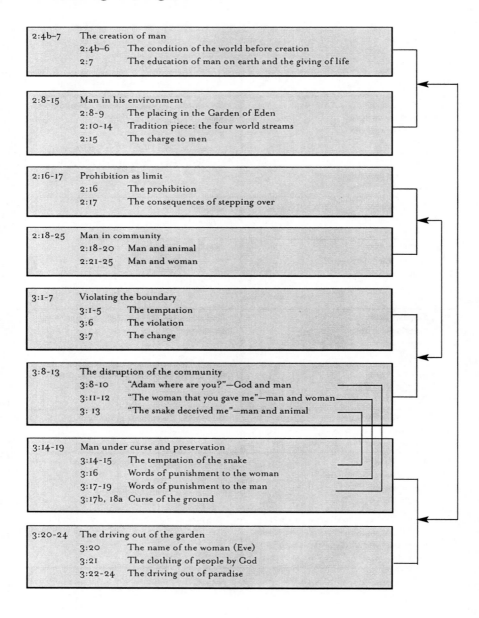

2:4b–7	The creation of man
2:4b–6	The condition of the world before creation
2:7	The education of man on earth and the giving of life

2:8–15	Man in his environment
2:8–9	The placing in the Garden of Eden
2:10–14	Tradition piece: the four world streams
2:15	The charge to men

2:16–17	Prohibition as limit
2:16	The prohibition
2:17	The consequences of stepping over

2:18–25	Man in community
2:18–20	Man and animal
2:21–25	Man and woman

3:1–7	Violating the boundary
3:1–5	The temptation
3:6	The violation
3:7	The change

3:8–13	The disruption of the community
3:8–10	"Adam where are you?"—God and man
3:11–12	"The woman that you gave me"—man and woman
3:13	"The snake deceived me"—man and animal

3:14–19	Man under curse and preservation
3:14–15	The temptation of the snake
3:16	Words of punishment to the woman
3:17–19	Words of punishment to the man
3:17b, 18a	Curse of the ground

3:20–24	The driving out of the garden
3:20	The name of the woman (Eve)
3:21	The clothing of people by God
3:22–24	The driving out of paradise

Table III. The Structure of the Nonpriestly Early History

Early history up until the flood (2:4b–6:4)	Early history after the flood (6:5–11:9)
Early history ancestor: Adam	Early history ancestor: Noah
The first generation (2:4b–3:24), especially 9:20-27: Adam/Noah as farmer, relationship to *adamah*, meaning of the fruit of the land for the transgression, opening of eyes and recognizing nakedness, curse of God/Noah	The first generation (6:5–8:22) ◄┐
The second generation: Cain and Abel (4:1-16): idea, working of the *adamah*, conflict and transgression, acceptance and curse of God	The second generation: Shem, Ham, Japheth (9:18-27): idea, development of *adamah*, conflict and transgression, acceptance and curse of Noah (after 8:21 no curse anymore)
Genealogy (4:17-26; 5:29): Urban culture	Genealogy (10): Nations
Human history (6:1-4): Violation of the boundary between humans and God (compare 3:5, 22-24: desire for the "good," violation and limitation of life span) "men of repute" (6:4), God's reflection and reaction (6:3), limits of human life span	Human history (11:1-9): Violation of the boundary between humans and God, "a name to make" (11:4), God's reflection and reaction (11:6-7; compare to 1 Psalm, pl. 3:22), limits of human reach

(According to David M. Carr, *Reading the Fractures of Genesis*, 233ff.)

Table IV. Relationships and Correspondences between Genesis 2–3; 4; 9; 10–11

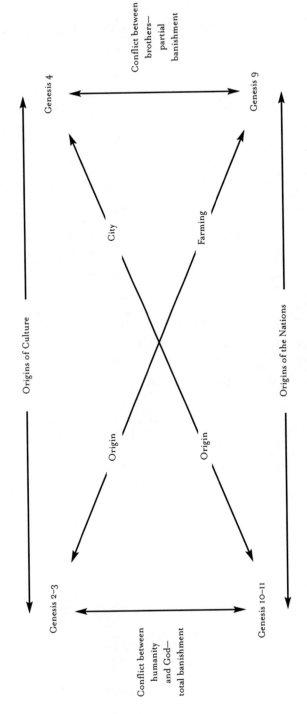

The origin of the *conditio humana* in relation to God between overstepping boundaries and preservation according to Genesis 23:9 and 10–11 (according to Carr, Reading the *Fractures of Genesis*, 233ff).

Figure 1. The Ancient Oriental Worldview (from Othmar Keel and Silvia Schroer, *Creation: Biblical Theology in Context of Ancient Oriental Religions* [Göttingen, 2002], 107).

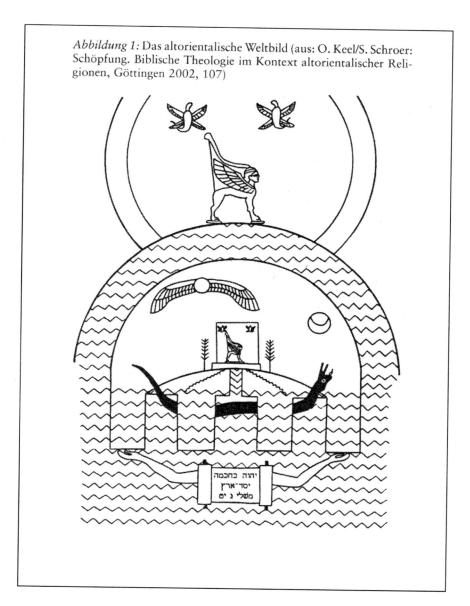

Abbildung 1: Das altorientalische Weltbild (aus: O. Keel/S. Schroer: Schöpfung. Biblische Theologie im Kontext altorientalischer Religionen, Göttingen 2002, 107)

Figure 2. The Peoples of the Earth According to Genesis 10 (from W. Zimmerli, "1 Moses 1–11: The Early History," in *Zurich Bible Commentary: OT* [Zürich 1967]).

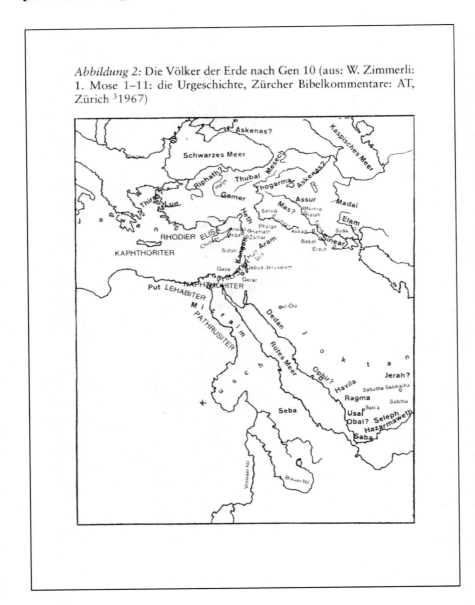

Abbildung 2: Die Völker der Erde nach Gen 10 (aus: W. Zimmerli: 1. Mose 1–11: die Urgeschichte, Zürcher Bibelkommentare: AT, Zürich ³1967)

Figure 3. The "Tower of Babel" (from Othmar Keel and Max Küchler, *Synoptic Texts from Genesis 2*, BB 8/2 [Fribourg, 1971], 163, section 15b).

Abbildung 3: Der „Turm zu Babel" (aus: O. Keel/M. Küchler: Synoptische Texte aus der Genesis II, BB 8/2, Fribourg 1971, 163 (Abb. 15b)).

NOTES

Introduction

1. Recent discussions on the hypotheses of the classical documents: Smend, *Entstehung*, 33–109; L. Schmidt, "Pentateuch," 88–109; Seebass, "Pentateuch." An overview of the more recent hypotheses can be found in Zenger, *Einleitung*, 66–176; Otto, "Pentateuch," 1089–102.

2. For the critical views, compare Zenger, *Einleitung*, and Otto, "Pentateuch," as well as Carr, *Reading*, 143–293. On the defense of a thorough reference of the sources outside of Smend, *Entstehung*, and L. Schmidt, "Pentateuch," compare Seebass, "Jahwist"; Levin, *Der Jahwist*.

3. Compare primarily Crüsemann, *Eigenständigkeit* (in discussion with Wolff, "Kerygma"); Steck argues differently concerning Genesis 12:1-3.

4. In addition to those mentioned in note 1, compare Zenger, "Priesterschrift."

5. In terms of commentaries, I have primarily relied on von Rad, *1 Mose*; Westermann, *Genesis I*, and Seebass, *Genesis I*. A short, very instructive introduction into the text can be found in Krauss and Küchler, *Erzählungen*.

I. Creation and Fall—The Beginning (1:1–3:24)

1. Compare Table I to this. In particular, note: W. H. Schmidt, *Schöpfungsgeschichte*, and Steck, *Schöpfungsbericht*.

2. The third and the sixth day each include two works of creation. Strictly speaking, the formula "and God said" appears nine times, but verse 29 apparently has no structural function.

3. Janowski, "Schöpfung," 970.

4. Compare W. H. Schmidt, *THAT* I, 336–39.

5. 2 Maccabees 7:28 first mentions a *creatio ex nihilo* (compare Rom. 4:17). According to W. H. Schmidt: "On the face of it, the verb does not describe a *creatio ex nihilo*, but it does indicate what, according to different ways of thinking, was assured by *creatio ex nihilo*: God's exceptional, sovereign, effortless, and completely free, unfettered act of creation" (*THAT* I, 338).

6. In the first part, *tohu* conveys the meaning in the semantic relationship to *wabohu*, which is connected merely by alliteration (also in Isa. 34:11; Jer. 4:23). Westermann, *Genesis I*, 142–43, sees *tohu* as having three nuances of meaning: (1) "desert": Deut. 32:10; Job 6:18; 12:14 = Ps. 107:46; (2) "barren," "wasteland": Isa. 24:10; 30:23; 34:11; Jer. 3; 4:23; (3) "nothingness": 1 Sam. 12:21; Isa. 14:17; 29:21; and so on. Job 26:7 is also revealing because here we get the entire range of the related concepts.

7. Bauks, *Die Welt vom Anfang*, 317.

8. Compare the "monument to Memphis theology" (Beyerlin, *RTAT*, 31–32; Eliade, *Schöpfungsmythen*, 83–84) and also Koch, *Wort*.

9. W. H. Schmidt, *Schöpfungsgeschichte*, 73; Levin, *Tatbericht*; in contrast Steck, *Schöpfungsbericht*, 32.

10. For literature on the worldview of the ancient Orient, see Keel and Schroer, *Schöpfung*; Janowski, "Weltbild."

11. Westermann, *Genesis I*, 166.

12. Compare Frettlöh, *Theologie des Segens*, 354–57.

13. Neumann-Gorsolke, *Herrschen*, 302; on the plural of *deliberationis* compare Seebass, *Genesis I*, 79.

14. Much has already been written recently regarding humankind's connection to God's likeness and lordship. Among these are: Koch, "Gestaltet die Erde"; Lohfink, "Macht euch die Erde untertan?"; Ebach, "Bild Gottes"; Janoswki, "Herrschaft über die Tiere"; Rüterswörden, *Dominium terrae*; Mathys, *Ebenbild Gottes*; and very comprehensive: Neumann-Gorsolke, *Herrschen*.

15. Contra Barth, *DK* III/1, 206, and Moltmann, *Schöpfung*, 228–29.

16. Neumann-Gorsolke, *Herrschen*, 303–15.

17. Also Frettlöh, *Theologie des Segens*, 358–66.

18. See primarily Zenger, *Gottes Bogen*, 90–96; Ebach, "Bild Gottes," 31–32. Neumann-Gorsolke, *Herrschen*, would like to translate the first of the verbs in 28a (kbŠ) not with "subdue, rule," but with "occupy" (as in a space), to "take possession of" the earth (274–99; 307).

19. See *Atram-hasis Mythos* I, 1–44, 194–97 (*TUAT* III, 618–19, 623; Keel and Schroer, *Schöpfung*, 242–43, compare also 241); *Enuma Elisch* VI, 5–8 (Eliade, *Schöpfungsmythen*, 145; Beyerlin, *RTAT*, 110; Keel and Schroer, 246); further texts in Eliade, 149; Keel and Schroer, 244.

20. Steck, *Welt*, 81.

21. Ibid., 80.

22. See Frettlöh, *Theologie des Segens*, 367–71; Moltmann, *Schöpfung*, 284–90.

23. Compare Barth, *KD* III/1, 243.

24. Janowski, *Tempel und Schöpfung*, especially 243.

25. Compare Carr, *ZAW*, 110, 159-72; Hieke, *Genealogien*, 48–49; Witte, *Urgeschichte*, 53–56; Koch, "Toledot-Formeln," 185.

26. There is an abundance of recent literature on the biblical creation passages. Named here by title are those that I used: Westermann, *Schöpfung*; Steck, *Welt und Umwelt*; L. Schmidt, *Schöpfung*; Ebach, "Schöpfung"; Löning and Zenger, *Als Anfang schuf Gott*; Keel and Schroer, *Schöpfung*; Kratz and Spieckermann, *Schöpfer/Schöpfung*; W. H. Schmidt, "Schöpfung"; Janowski, "Schöpfung."

27. Compare Schmid, *Gerechtigkeit*; also his "Schöpfung."

28. Statement by Jörg Barthel; compare Janowski, *Königtum Gottes*, 170, 206–12; *Schöpfung*, 971; Spieckermann, *Heilsgegenwart*, 21–49; 180–85; Bauks, "Chaos"; Löning/Zenger, *Als Anfang*, 49–64.

29. Exemplary and very formative for more than a generation is von Rad, "Das theologische Problem." On the influences of the time and political background of this thesis, compare Ebach, "Schöpfung," 103–4; Löning/Zenger, *Als Anfang*, 13–16.

30. So for example Rendtorff, *Theologie des Alten Testaments* II, 7–19.

31. Compare to this Eliade, *Schöpfungsmythen*; Beyerlin, *RTAT*; Kaiser (ed.), *TUAT* III, 3/4; Linke, *Schöpfungsmythologie*; Keel and Schroer, *Schöpfung*, Müller, *Mythos* and *Schöpfungsmythen*.

32. Compare the "Denkmal memphitisicher Theologie" (Beyerlin, *RTAT*, 32; Eliade, *Schöpfungsmythen*, 83–85), also Koch, *Wort*.

33. Marduk says: "I will create a being, a man. To him I assign the work of the gods in order to lighten their load"; Tablet VI, 5–9, 31–40 (Eliade, *Schöpfungsmythen*, 145–46; Beyerlin, *RTAT*, 110); this is similar to *Atram-hasis Mythos* I, 195. The gods speak to the mother goddess Mami: "Create early man so that he can take the burden off of you! He will take up the burden, the work of the Enlil; man shall carry the basket of the gods" (TUAT III/4, 623).

34. *Merikare P*, 130–38, according to Assmann, *Agypten*, 72 (compare also 201–2); Beyerlin, *RTAT*, 72; compare also Hornung, *Der Eine*, 34–35, 128.

35. Compare the overview in Stolz, *Einführung*.

36. Compare the debate in Assmann, *Mose*, which he continues with modifications and explanations in his *Die mosaische Unterscheidung* (in connection with important contributions to the discussion by Koch, Rendtorff, Zenger, et al.); compare also Söding, *Ist der Glaube Feind der Freiheit?*

37. Assmann, *Mosaische Unterscheidung*, 100 (which talks about "cosmotheism").

38. Werbick, "Absolutistischer Eingottglaube," 173.

39. Assmann, *Mosaische Unterscheidung*, 100.

40. Hemminger and Hemminger, *Jenseits der Weltbilder*, 80; compare also Pannenberg, *Systematische Theologie* II, 141–42.

41. Hemminger and Hemminger, *Jenseits der Weltbilder*, 81; Bosshard, *Erschafft die Welt*, 167–68.

42. Compare Deissler, *Schöpfungsgeschichte*, 182, with four answers to the question "Why do believing scientists love Genesis 1?" and additionally the warning of Moses, *Schöpfungaussagen*, 67–68, with its naive attempt at harmonizing.

43. On the anthropological principle, compare Breuer, *Das anthropische Prinzip*; Barrow and Tipler, *The Anthropic Cosmological Principle*, 86–87.

44. On the five events leading to the dying out of the masses, compare Leakey and Lewin, *Ursprung*, 350–51; on the principle of the egoistic genes, compare Dawkins, *Das egoistische Gen*.

45. Different from Duve, *Aus Staub geboren*, 456–57.

46. That appears to have been the actual temptation in Darwin's faith in God. Compare the citation in Dawkins, *Ein Fluss in Eden*, 111, which makes the question of the apparent meaninglessness of the suffering of creatures the axis point of his atheistic conviction (*aaO*, 151).

47. Heim, *Weltschöpfung*, 103.

48. Ebach, "Bild Gottes," 36.
49. See page 13 and especially Carr, *Reading*, 75.
50. Compare also Löning and Zenger, *Als Anfang schuf Gott*, 139, which high-lights the parallels between Genesis 2, 4:7, and 5:1.
51. See pages xii–xiv.
52. Compare Zenger, *Einleitung*, 162–76; Carr, *Reading*, 233.
53. Westermann, *Genesis I*, 60; Bauks, *Die Welt am Anfang*, 276–79.
54. However, in the OT "clay" and "dust" can be parallel (Job 10:9; compare Lev. 14:42), compare Keel and Schroer, *Schöpfung*, 144–45.
55. Westermann stresses this in *Genesis I*, 276–81.
56. So says Stoebe, *THAT* I, 658–60; Steck, *Paradieserzählung*, 43; Albertz, *Ihr werdet sein*, 93.
57. Westermann, *Genesis I*, 337.
58. Compare Höver-Johag, *ThWAT* III, 329–30.
59. Winter, *Lebensbaum*, 155.
60. Keel and Schroer, *Schöpfung*, 153; Dohmen, *Schöpfung*, 323.
61. Thus, Westermann in *Genesis I*, 261.
62. This is clearly worked out in Albertz, *Ihr werdet sein*.
63. Thus, Westermann in *Genesis I*, 350.
64. Otto, "Woher weiß der Mensch," 229.
65. Compare Heidegger, *Sein und Zeit*, 249–55; on placement in ancient orien-tal thinking, compare Assmann, *Tod und Jenseits*, 6.
66. Steck, *Paradieserzählung*, 127.
67. That is true, despite many similarities, also for the Atram-hasis epic (com-pare the table in Carr, *Reading*, 242–43). Bosshard, *Erschafft die Welt*, 176, speaks about a "suitable scrap" that was used.
68. Pagels, *Adam, Eva und die Schlange*, 144–69.
69. Compare Lichtenberger, *Das Ich Adams*, 121–35.
70. However, the Papal Bible Commission in 1909 still described Genesis 1–3 as "stories about actual events that took place" that could be researched using "par-ticular scientific language" from which their linguistically historical meaning could not be excluded (*DH*, 3512–519). Compare the more recent bulletin of the International Theological Commission of the Vatican: "Communion and Stewardship: Human Persons Created in the Image of God," §§62-70 (La Civaltá Cattolica, 2004, IV, 254–86).
71. Kante, *Werke*, 9, 92.
72. Drewermann, *Strukturen des Bösen* III, 88, in reference to Hegel, *Philosophie der Religion* II (*SW* 18), 260; see also Welker, *Schöpfung*, 108–17.
73. Kierkegaard, *Begriff Angst*, 39–41; compare Drewermann, *Strukturen des Bösen* III, 436.
74. Kierkegaard, *Begriff Angst*, 46 (English version, 49).
75. Compare Drewermann, *Stukturen des Bösen* II, 115–18; Jork, *Sexualität*, 50.
76. Drewermann, *Stukturen des Bösen* II, 117.
77. Compare Drewermann, *Strukturen des Bösen* II, 130–31, and Jork, *Sexualität*, 50–51, in which the symbolism fluctuates unhampered. However, the exegete Seebass insists that the story can only be understood if one refers back to the fact

that in the Hebrew grammar the snake is male, which forces the resulting translation as "the gulp" (*Genesis I*, 100).

78. Drewermann, *Stukturen des Bösen* II, 131.
79. Ibid., 139.
80. Ibid.
81. Dieter Wyss in the foreword to Arnold-Carey, *Und sie erkannten*, 5.
82. Ibid., 131.
83. Albertz, *Ihr werdet sein*, 109; compare also Otto, "Woher weiß der Mensch," 229–30.
84. Steck, *Paradieserzählung*, 124–25.
85. Richter, *Gotteskomplex*, 228.
86. Compare to this also Gestrich, *Wiederkehr*, 257–83; Pannenberg, *Systematische Theologie* II, 226–302; Sattler and Schneider, "Schöpfungslehre," 227–30.
87. Compare 1 Timothy 2:13-14; compare Sirach 25:24; Apocalypse of Moses 14.
88. Compare Käsemann, *Romans*, 140.
89. Wisdom 2:24; Apocalypse of Moses 32; 3 Ezra 7:116-18.
90. Wilken, *Romans* II, 40.
91. Compare also Cavalli-Sforza and Cavalli-Sforza, *Verschieden und doch gleich*; Dawkins, *Ein Fluss in Eden*; Kealey and Lewin, *Ursprung*, 228–46; de Duve, *Aus Staube geboren*, 354–55.
92. Compare International Theological Commission, *Communion and Stewardship*, 64.
93. The Neanderthal may not have had this ability because of the anatomy of the larynx, which lacked differentiation in the brain (Gregersen, "Mensch," 1048); compare Leakey and Lewin, *Ursprung*, 276–79.
94. Compare Wilson, *Biologie*, 169; Voland and Söling, "Basis"; Euler, "Religion." On the beginning of religion in the early history of humanity, compare Ohlig, *Religion*, 28.
95. Compare Eccles, *Rätsel Mensch*, 230; also Robinson, *Wunder des Menschseins*, 39–71, a version that corresponds exactly to the position of the International Theological Commission (in *Communion and Stewardship*, 63–64) represented by the Catholic Church.
96. Compare Dawkins, *Das egoistische Gen*, 321–22.
97. Leakey and Lewin, *Ursrpung*, 347–48.
98. Ibid.
99. The *volvox* types are cell colonies of green algae, which on the basis of their division of labor are categorized as genuine multiple-cell organisms. However, "only a one-cell organism has a potential for immortality, since its cell division under special conditions over thousands of generations from now does not show any signs of processes for alteration" (*Große Brockhaus*, sv. Tod).
100. Compare Mohr, *Natur und Moral*, 93.
101. Different in Pannenberg, *Syst. Theologie* II, 310–11.
102. Härle, *Dogmatik*, 488–89.
103. Assmann, *Mosaische Unterscheidung*, 100.
104. *HerKorr* 6, 1951/52, 168–69.

105. The classical representation of the "standard model" is found in Weinberg, *Drei Minuten*. More recent renderings are found in Audretsch, *Vom Anfang der Welt* 66–113), and Weidemann, "Entstehung der Welt"—both of which, from a scientific view, leave the question of God open—and very comprehensively in Dorschner, *Mensch*, 7–145. Dorschner argues that "the ideas of certain scientists regarding the God question should be more strongly situated in the theological discussion." Critical of this are Audretsch, *Vom Anfang*, 113; Barbour, *Wissenschaft*, 280–81; Goenner, "Urknallbild," 36. The cosmological alternatives to the standard model are argued in Fahr, "Alternativen."

106. *Vom Gottesstaat*, DeCiv Dei XI, 6.

107. Breuere, *Anthorpische Prinzip*, 23–24; Barrow and Tipler, *Anthropic Principle*, 16, 21.

108. Compare the positive assessment in Schockenhoff, *Kosmologie*, 137–40; Benz, *Zukunft*, 111–14; the differentiated representative in Kanitschneider, "Naturphilosophie" and *Mechanistische Welt*, 149–59, and the critical position of Hawking, *Geschichte*, 157–61, and Barbour, *Wissenschaft*, 286–88.

109. Barrow and Tipler, *Anthropic Principle*, 22. Weckwerth, "Anthropsiche Prinzip," dares that even in the "religious principle of the cosmos" the "observer capable of religion 'produces'" (66) through a "structural informational deficit" that leads to the construction of faith, hope, and love (67).

110. Stadelman, *Im Herzen der Materie*, 80: "In the known living being . . . is the world spirit itself known." Compare Hegel, *Phenomenology of Spirit*, 585: "Rather, the spirit does not in itself, not as world spirit, complete itself, since it cannot as self-conscious spirit reach its own completion."

111. Wegter-McNelly, "Quantenphysik," 1859.

112. Compare Ganoczy, *Chaos*, and thus critical Achtner, *Chaostheorie*, 46–48; on the meaning of an "open system" compare Prigogine and Stengers, *Dialog*; Altner, *Welt als offenes System*; Link, *Schöpfung*, 439.

113. Z. B. Monod, *Zufall*; Dawkins, *Der blinde Uhrmacher*; as physicist Weinberg, *Traum*, 251–70; on the phenomena compare Polkinghorne, *An Gott glauben*, 19–20.

114. *Finding Darwin's God*, 269 and 268. The philosopher Weissmahr argues in a similar vein. For him, the "free dimension" of evolution supports the thesis that the teaching of evolution implies "an argument for the existence of God" ("Evolution," 87–88).

115. I name particularly Trefil, Davies, von Ditfurth, Ferguson, and so on.

116. I will name several in the order of their appearance: Gutsche, Hägele, and Hafner, *Schöpfung und Evolution*; Böhme, *Evolution und Gottesglaube*; Audretsch and Mainzer, *Vom Anfant der Welt*; Schmitz-Moormann, *Schöpfung und Evolution*; Gräb, *Urknall oder Schöpfung?*; Dorschner, Heller, and Pannenberg, *Mensch und Universum*; Fuchs and Kessler, *Gott, der Kosmos und die Freiheit*; Dürr et al., *Gott, der Mensch und die Wissenschaft*; Hilper and Hasenhüttl, *Schöpfung und Selbstorganisation*; Weingartner, *Evolution als Schöpfung*; Schockenhoff and Huber, *Gott und der Urknall*; Lüke, Schnakenberg, and Souvignier, *Darwin und Gott*; Müller, *Kosmologie*.

117. Here are Peacocke, Polkinghorne, and Lüke to be named, but also scientists like Benze and the Hemminger brothers, and theologians like Moltmann, Link, Welkner, and above all Pannenberg!

118. Daecke, "Schöpfung"; compare also Lüke, *Schöpfung als Evolution?* and *Bio-Theologie*, 109–65.

119. Gitt, *Schuf Gott durch Evolution?*; Wilder Smith, *Die Naturwissenschaften*.

120. Compare Monod, *Zufall*; Dawkins, *Der blinde Uhrmacher*; Wilson, *Biologie*; Wuketits, *Evolutionstheorien*, 27; Hawking, *Kurze Geschichte*, 213.

121. For example, Illies, *Der Jahrhundertirrtum*, 188–89, and *Schöpfung*, 89; Vollmert, *Das Molekül*, 26–27. These distinctions are to some extent missing in the book by Jeßberger, *Kreationismus*.

122. Rahner, "Naturwissenschaft," 26.

123. Compare Dürr, *Physik und Transzendenz*, 21–41 (Planck), 67–78 (Einstein), 295–336 (Heisenberg).

124. Mutschler, *Physik* and "Welterklärung."

125. On the theme of "self-organization and creation" compare Bosshardt, *Erschafft die Welt sich selbst?*; Hilpert and Hasenhüttl, *Schöpfung und Selbstorganisation*; on the concept of intelligent design compare Peters and Hewlett, *Evolution*, 93–114.

126. Jantsch, *Selbstorganisation*, 412.

127. Compare especially Barbour, *Wissenschaft*.

128. Ibid., 404–5.

129. Whitehead, *Prozess und Realität*, 626.

130. Barbour, *Wissenschaft*, 406.

131. Whitehead, *Prozess*, 621; on the critical discussion compare Link, *Schöpfung*, 428–38.

132. Polkinghorne, *An Gott glauben*, 30–31, 53–77.

133. Peacocke, *Gottes Wirken*, 161–62, and *Paths*, 57–58; compare Moltmann, *Schöpfung*, 109.

134. Compare Babour, *Wissenschaft*, 342–43; Bosshardt, *Erschafft die Welt*, 154.

135. Polkinghorne, *An Gott glauben*, 65–75.

136. Peacocke, *Gottes Wirken*, 51–61; Schmitz-Moormann, *Materie*, 184–85.

137. Pannenberg, *Syst. Theologie* II, 99–104, and *Gott*, 206–7.

138. So also notes Peters and Hewlett, *Evolution*, 150–55.

139. Daecke, "Schöpfung," 92–93.

140. Compare Peacocke, *Paths*, 1–2.

141. Compare Barbour, *Wissenschaft*, 309; Pannenberg, *Syst. Theologie* II, 91–92.

142. Compare Bosshard, *Erschafft die Welt*, 167, 191.

143. Compare Ebach, "Bild Gottes," 36; Pannenberg, *Syst. Theologie* II, 162–201. On the "timeless" and "timeliness" characters of God's creating activity compare Lüke, "Schöpfung aus dem Nichts," 48–50.

144. On this and the following compare Löning and Zenger, *Als Anfang*.

145. Trefil, *Augenblick*, 267.

146. Davies, *Gott*, 286; compare Davies, *Plan Gottes*, 212.

147. Jantsch, *Selbstorganisation*, 412.

148. Stadelmann, *Im Herzen*, 81.

149. von Ditfurth, *Wir sind nicht nur von dieser Welt*, 145–46.

150. Compare the outline in Pannenberg, *Syst. Theologie* II, 34; Moltmann, *Schöpfung*, 106; Link, *Schöpfung*, 528; Schmitz-Moormann, *Materie*, 166; Jüngel, *Gott als Geheimnis*, 514.

151. Jüngel, *Geheimnis*, 302–3; Schmitz-Moormann, *Materie*, 163.

II. Power and History—The First Steps (4:1–6:4)

1. Compare Seebass, *Genesis I*, 148; on the use of euphemism, see Schottroff, *THAT* I, 691.

2. Seebass, *Genesis I*, 143, 152–53.

3. Westermann, *Genesis I*, 410.

4. Crüsemann, *Autonomie*, 65, paraphrases in a similar way: "When what you know and think of as good, wholesome, and useful results in good consequences, then you are proud."

5. Thus, Knierin, *Hauptbegriffe*, 58.

6. In contrast to the interpretation of sin as a demonic power, Janowski turns to 4:7b and refers to Abel, who is the reason for Cain's offense and about whom Cain should concern himself (= rule); "Jenseits von Eden," 148–f; "Kain und Abel," 737.

7. Janowski, "Jenseits von Eden," 149–50, translates: "Then Cain told Abel . . ."

8. Compare Westermann, *Genesis I*, 418.

9. Compare Knierim, *Hauptbegriffe*, 221–22; compare 193–94, 252–53.

10. Seebass, *Genesis I*, 159.

11. Westermann, *Genesis I*, 424.

12. Janoswki, "Jenseits von Eden," 152. Earlier interpreters saw in Cain's fate an etiological explanation of the nomadic existence of the Canaanites, which is derived from Cain in Numbers 24:22 (compare Judges 1:16; 1 Sam 15:6; 27:10; 30:29). There is, however, no real evidence for this; compare Zwickel, "Keniter," 729).

13. Compare to this Janowski, "Jenseits von Eden," 152–53.

14. See Crüsemann, "Autonomie und Sünde," 66.

15. Lorenz, *Das sogenannte Böse* (especially 155, 371); continued in Eibl-Eibesfeldt, *Biologie*, 516–95; and Wickler, *Biologie der zehn Gebote*, 73–96.

16. Goodall, *Ein Herz für Schimpansen* (*The Chimpanzees I Love*), 118–33; Vogel, *Vom Töten zum Mord*, 117–21.

17. Sommer and Amann, *Die großen Menschenaffen* (*The Great Apes*), 79.

18. Mohr, *Natur und Moral*, 105.

19. Vogel, *Vom Töten zum Mord*, 127–28, cited by Thomas H. Huxley.

20. Dawkins, *Das egoistische Gen*, 322; in English, *The Selfish Gene*, 200–201.

21. Wilson, *Einheit*, 351; compare the different discussions in Wickler and Seibt, *Prinzip Eigennutz*, 264–65, 279–80.

22. Eibl-Eibesfeldt, *Biologie*, 595, 571.

23. Leakey and Lewin, *Ursprung*, 242.

24. Sommer, "Töten von Artgenossen," 94; Vogel, *Vom Töten zum Mord*, 125.

25. Crüsemann, *Autonomie*, 69.

26. Compare also Kutsch, *Das posse non peccare*.

27. I use here the arguments from Pannenberg, *Aggression*, 161–73.

28. Compare Westermann, *Genesis I*, 144.

29. Thus, ibid., 448–49.

30. So Janowski, "Jenseits von Eden," 153.

31. Compare Westermann, *Genesis I*, 457.

32. Compare von Rad, *Erstes Buch Mose*, 92.

33. Perhaps this was originally the title of the first small book, which contained further similar records and which the priestly writings worked into their stories (compare 10:1; 11:10, 27; 25:12; 36:1; Exod. 6:14); so also von Rad, *Erstes Buch Mose*, 55; Carr, *Reading*, 71–72, and *ZAW* 110, 169–70; in contrast, Westermann, *Genesis I*, 481–82; Seebass, *Genesis I*, 179.

34. On this, Westermann, *Genesis I*, 486.

35. Compare Herrmann, "Henoch/Henochschriften."

36. Compare Westermann, *Genesis I*, 487.

37. Compare the lists in Seebass, *Genesis I*, 178–79.

38. In the Sumerian, lists of divine kings before the flood have very high numbers of years attributed to their reigns (up to 43,200 years). For the most part, any direct influence of these lists on the biblical version is rejected (see Westermann, *Genesis I*, 473–76; although Seebass, *Genesis I*, 182–83, thinks that an "indirect occurrence" was possible). However, a similar tendency could be behind this—namely, to underscore the significance of the period.

39. Krauss and Küchler, *Erzählungen*, 136.

40. Significantly, the Babylonian flood story in the Atram-hasis epic begins with the same motif: "Twelve hundred years had not passed that the land continued to grow and mankind continued to be more numerous" (Tablet II, I, 1: *TUAT* III, 629). Consequently, many interpreters also see in this story the introduction of a biblical flood story. It is correct that in the biblical account of 6:1 there is also evidence of a clear break. However, 6:5 resumes the story again with new content.

41. See Seebass, *Genesis I*, 192–93.

42. On the difficulty of translating, see ibid., 193.

43. Ibid., 198.

44. According to Gese, *Lebensbaum*, 110–11, that is the point of the story.

45. Baumgart, *Umkehr*, 565 (compare 110–50).

III. Law and Grace—The Crisis (6:5–9:17)

1. An overview is offered by Westermann, *Genesis I*, 536–46.

2. See especially Whitcomb and Morris, *Die Sinflut*.

3. I use von Soden's spelling in *TUAT* III/4, 612–45; another transcription is in the Atram-hasis.

4. The text can be found in the German translation in Beyerlin, *RTAT*, 114–21 (Schmökel), and in *TUAT* III/4, 626–45 (von Soden), 728–35 (Hecker).

5. On the question as to whether the noise of humankind was caused only by their large numbers or by noisy rebellion, compare the works by Moran, *Magic Word*, 33–86, on the one hand, and von Soden, "Der Mensch," on the other. The Gilgamesh epic gives no basis in terms of content for the decision of the flood. It says in XI, 14: "It was the gods' idea to cause a flood."

6. I use the symbol *J* for the early priestly tradition.

7. Compare the overview in Westermann, *Genesis I*, 532–35.

8. Recently, these verses have been attributed to edits that occurred after the priestly writings; compare Krüger, "Das menschliche Herz," 74–76; Arneth, "Sintflut," 1346.

9. Seebass, *Genesis I*, 208.

10. Fundamental to the theme is Jeremias, *Die Reue Gottes*.

11. Compare Seebass, *Genesis I*, 208–9.

12. Peacocke, "Natur und Gott," 181.

13. Stoebe, *THAT* I, 585.

14. Westermann, *Genesis I*, 560.

15. Kessler, "Gott, der kosmische Prozess und die Freiheit," 225–26.

16. Stoebe, *THAT* I, 585.

17. Gertz, "Bund," 1864.

18. Compare Westermann, *Genesis I*, 572–73.

19. Compare ibid., 595.

20. Ibid., 597.

21. Ibid., 608–9; Seebass, *Genesis I*, 221.

22. Compare Keller, *THAT* II, 646.

23. Pannenberg, *Gott als Schöpfer*, 203.

24. Zenger, *Gottes Bogen*, 117; also Ebach, "Bild Gottes," 31–32.

25. Zenger, *Gottes Bogen*, 118.

26. Ebach, "Bild Gottes," 45; compare Westermann, *Genesis I*, 623.

27. A responsible animal ethic must thus not necessarily lead to vegetarianism, but it is in any case a result of the premise that life should be treated reverently.

28. Compare Gertz, "Bund," 1965.

29. See Zenger, *Gottes Bogen*, 124–31.

30. Westermann (*Genesis I*, 634) categorically rejects this. It is by its representatives also interpreted in various ways: either as a sign of the continual lordship of God analogous to the iconography of ancient oriental kings, or as a symbol that God hung a bow of war in the sky to make peace with the earth.

31. Westermann, *Genesis I*, 635.

32. Compare Wandrey, "Noachidische Gebote," 348–49.

33. As far as I can tell, there is no historical interpretative research of the flood story.

34. Ziegler, *Der schwäbsiche Lindwurm*, 54–55.

35. Dawkins, *Ein Fluss in Eden*, 151.

36. Woolley, *Ur in Chaldea*.

37. Also see verses 35 and 36.

38. Baumgart, *Umkehr*, 419–95, 569.

39. Compare ibid., 566.

40. Ibid., 564.

41. Johann Jakob Schütz, "Sei Lob und Her," EG 326, 3.

IV. Variety and Confusion—The Expansion (9:18–11:26)

1. Primarily Baumgart, *Umkehr*, 9–102.

2. Blum, "Urgeschichte," 437.

3. If one views the *toledot* formula as a structural hallmark for the "early history" chapter of the entire work, then there are four sections: 1:1–2:3; 2:4–4:26; 5:1–9:29; 10:1–11:26.

4. Compare the discussion concerning the related questions in Westermann, *Genesis I*, 646–49.

5. It is interesting that also in Genesis 19, in the story of the destruction of Sodom and Gomorra and the saving of Lot, which contains many parallels to the flood story, is also followed by a similar "scandalous" story line where it tells the story of Lot's daughters, also suggesting genealogical connections concerning the two neighboring peoples of Israel; namely, the Moabites and the Ammonites.

6. Evidence cited in Westermann, *Genesis I*, 652–53.

7. Compare Krauss and Küchler, *Erzählungen*, 173, under the title "Ein Abriß der Geschichte des Nahen Ostens?"

8. Seebass, *Genesis I*, 250; similar in Westermann, *Genesis I*, 655–57.

9. Westermann, *Genesis I*, 661.

10. In a similar vein it is indirectly stated that Canaan becomes Japheth's servant as a result, since he finds "a lot of space" in Shem's tent!

11. Westermann, *Welt und Mensch*, 113.

12. Regarding the identifications here and in the following, compare Westermann, *Genesis I*, 673–704; Seebass, *Genesis I*, 256–64.

13. In the Masoretic text there is mention of the Casluhites, whom we cannot identify. Because of Amos 9:7, many interpreters, and also the Luther translation, attribute this remark to the Kaftorites.

14. In Japheth, the chronology is different; whether other things were consciously emphasized or were simply varied is unclear.

15. See Cavalli-Sforza and Cavalli-Sforza, *Verschieden*, 117, 175–206. This work also treats the question of the connection between genetic, ethical, and linguistic "branches" of humanity (259–314).

16. Compare Crüsemann, *Menschheit und Volk*, 193–94.

17. Ibid., 192–94.

18. Thus also in the Sumerian epic *Enmerkar and the Lord of Aratta* the hope is for "confusion of language" in the coming of the time of peace, in which the god Enki will transform all available languages in the mouths of humankind to one language for human beings so that they can praise Enlil; see Beyerlin, *RTAT*, 112–13.

19. Compare the overview of Westermann, *Genesis I*, 711–18.

20. Compare Seebass, *Genesis I*, 271–74.

21. So the report of the Nabopolassar on the reestablishment of the Etemenanki, the ziggurat of the Marduk temple Esagila in Babylon (*TUAT* II, 492), and Nebuchadnezzar II, who has finished the construction, write: "I set my hand to praise Etemenanki, to have her skin touch the heavens" (according to Uehlinger, *Weltreich*, and "a speech," 336).

22. Compare von Soden, "Etemenanki"; otherwise Uehlinger, *Weltreich*, who sought to refute this deduction (201–19) and regarded the incomplete city of Dur-Sharrukin (Sargonsburg), which Sargon II (728–705 B.C.) wanted to make the capitol of his realm, as a model for the oldest part of the story (470–445 B.C.).

23. Seebass, *Genesis I*, 278.

24. Thus, above all the interpretation of Uehlinger, *Weltriech*, 406–512.

25. Von Rad, *Erstes Buch Mose*, 126. (Crüsemann, *Menschheit*, 193, cited von Rad abbreviated and from one vantage point! Compare von Rad, *Theologie I*, 165, 167.)

26. On an alternative "punishment" or "reactualized blessing," compare Uehlinger, *Weltreich*, 572–84. It is fascinating in this context to follow the linguistic discussion on the early language of humanity, which was differentiated as the earth was settled (compare Victorri, *Ursprache*).

27. A schedule can be found in Seebass, *Genesis I*, 289.

28. Wolff, "Das Kerygma des Jahwisten."

29. Crüsemann, *Eigenständigkeit*; Carr, *Reading*, 143–293.

30. See Steck, "Genesis 12:1-3."

31. Compare Frettlöh, *Theologie des Segens*, 288–302.

Conclusion

1. Hawking, *Kurze Geschichte* (*A Brief History of Time*), 217.

2. So primarily in the *Enuma Elish* (Eliade, *Schöpfungsmythen*, 134–45).

3. Compare Blum, "Urgeschichte," 439–40, who gives a wonderful summary of the early history of the nonpriestly writings.

4. Ibid., 440.

5. Compare Zenger, *Einleitung*, 165.

6. Blum, "Urgeschichte," 442.

7. Zenger, *Preisterschrift*, 441.

8. Janowski, *Tempel*, 244.

9. Thus, Mutschler, *Physik, Religion, New Age*.

10. Miller, *Finding Darwin's God*, 165–91.

11. Davies, *Gott*, 15, 294.

12. Weinberg, *Die ersten drei Minuten*, 212.

13. A connection between humanity's freedom to decide and the not-yet-determined course of the quantum area, especially the not-determined course of evolution—something that is acknowledged by many researchers—appears to me questionable (compare Miller, *Finding Darwin's God*, 238–39, 252–53; Schmitz-Moormann, *Materie*, 189–98; Kessler, *Gott*, 225–26; Peacocke, *Paths*, 75–90).

BIBLIOGRAPHY

The herein cited literature is in the notes by name and abbreviated title cited. The abbreviations are aligned with the abbreviation bibliography in the *Theological Real Encyclopedia* 1994.

Achter, Wolfgang. *Die Chaostheorie*, EZW-Texte, 1997, 135.

Albertz, Rainer. *"Ihr werdet sein wie Gott": Gen 3:1-7 on the Background of the OT and the Sumerian-Babylonian View of Men*, WO 24, 1993, 89–111.

Altner, Günter. "Die Evolutionstheorie als historische und aktuelle grundlage für das Gespräch zwischen Theologie und Naturwissenschaft," in *Die andere Hälfte der Wahrheit*, ed. J. Audretsch, Munich, 1992, 56–71.

———, ed. *Die Welt des offense System: Eine Kontroverse um das Werk von Ilya Prigogine*, Frankfurt am Main, 1986.

———. *Okologische Theologie, Perspektiven zur Orientierung*, Stuttgart, 1989.

Arneth, Martin. "Sintflut," RGG VII, 2004, 1344–46.

Arnold-Carey, Lieselotte. *Und sie erkannteen, dass sie nackt waren, Geschlechtswahrnehmung und kindliche Entwicklung*, Göttingen, 1972.

Assmann, Jan. *Agypte: Theologie und Frömmigkeit einer Hochkultur*, Stuttgart, 1991.

———. *Die Mosaische Unterschedung oder der Preis des Monotheismus*, Munich/Vienna, 2003.

———. *Moses der Agypter: Die Entzifferung einer Gedächtnisspur*, Munich/Vienna, 1998.

———. *Tod und Jenseits im Alten Agypten*, Munich, 2001.

Audretsch, Jürgen, ed. *Die andere Hälfte der Wahrheit: Naturwissenschaft, Philosophie, Religion*, Munich, 1992.

———, and Klaus Mainzer, ed. *Vom Anfang der Welt—Wissenschaft, Philosophie, Religion, Mythos*, Munich, 1990.

———, and Hans Weder. *Kosmologie und Kreativität: Theologie und Naturwissenschaft im Dialog*, ThLZ, F1, Leipzig, 1999.

Barbour, Ian G. *Wissenschaft und glaube*, RthN 1, Göttingen, 2003 (2005).

Barrow, John D., and Frank J. Tipler. *The Anthropic Cosmological Principle*, Oxford, 1986.

Barth, Karl. *Kirchliche Dogmatik 3. Band: Die Lehre von der Schöpfung*, part 1 (*KD* III/1), Zollikon-Zürich, 1945.

Bibliography

Bauks, Michaela. "'Chaos' als Metapher für die Gefährdung der Weltordnung" in *Das biblische Weltbild und seine altorientalischen Kontexte*, ed. B. Janowski and B. Ego, FAT 32, Tübingen 2001, 431–64.

———. *Die Welt am Anfang: Zum Verständnis von Vorwelt und Weltentstehung in Gen 1 und in der altorientalischen Literatur*, WMANT 74, Nekirchen-Vluyn, 1997.

Baumgart, Norbert Clemens. *Die Umkehr der Schöpfergottes: Zur Komposition und religionsgeschichtlichem Hintergrund von Gen 5–9*, HBS 22, Freiburg i. Br. u.a., 1999.

Benz, Arnold. *Die Zukunft des Universums: Zufall, Chaos, Gott?* Düsseldorf, 1997.

Beyerlin, Walter, ed. *Religionsgeschichtliches Textubch zum Alten Testament (RTAT)*, ATD-E/GAT 1, Göttingen, 1985.

Blum, Erhard. "Urgescihchte," *TRE* 34, 2002, 436–45.

Böhme, Wolfgang, ed. *Evolution und Gottesglaube*, Göttingen, 1988.

Bosshard, Stefan Niklaus. *Erschafft die Welt sich selbst? Die Selbst-organisation von Natur und Mensch aus naturwissenschaftlicher, philosophischer und theologischer Sicht*, QD 103, Freiburg i. Br. u.a., 1985.

Bresch, Carsten, Sigurd M. Daecke, and Helmut Riedlinger, eds. *Kann man Gott aus der Natur erkennen?* Freiburg i. B. us.a., 1990.

Breuer, Reinhard. *Das anthropsiche Prinzip*, Frankfurt a.m., 1984.

Carr, David M. Βίβγος γενέσεως Revisited: A Synchronic Analysis of Patterns in *Genesis as Part of the Torah*, ZAW 110, 1998, 159–72, 327–47.

———. *Reading the Fractures of Genesis: Historical and Literary Approaches*, Louisville, 1996.

Cavalli-Sforza, Luca, and Francesco Cavalli-Sforza. *Verscheiden und doch gleich: Ein Genetiker entizeht dem Rassismus die Grundlage*, Munich, 1994.

Crüsemann, Frank. "Autonomie und Sünde: Gen 4:7 und die jahwistische Urgeshichte" in *Traditionene der Befreiung*, Vol. 1, ed. W. Schottroff and W. Stegemann, Munich, 1980, 60–77.

———. "Die eigenständigkeit der Urgeschichte: Ein beitrag zur Diskussion um den 'Jahwisten,'" in *Die Botschaft und die Boten* (FS, H. W. Wolff), ed. J. Jeremias and L. Perlitt, Neurkirchen-Vluyn 1981, 11–29.

———. *Menschheit und volk: Israels selbstdefinition im genealogischen System der Genesis*, EvTh 58, 180–95.

Daecke, Sigurd Martin. "Schöpfung als Interpretation von evolution-Evolution als Konkretion von Schöpfung," in *Evolution als Schöpfung*, ed. P. Weingartner, Stuttgart u.a., 2001, 73–96.

Davies, Paul. *Der Plan Gottes: Die Rätsel unserer existenz unddie Wissenschaft*, Frankfurt a.m. Leipzig, 1995.

———. *Gott und die moderne Physik*, Munich, 1989.

Dawkins, Richard. *Das egoistische Gen*, Heidelberg u.a., 1994.

———. *Der blinde Uhrmacher*, Munich, 1987.

———. *Und es entsprang ein Fluss in Eden: Das Uhrwerk der evolution*, Munich, 1996.

De Duve, Christian. *Aus Staub geboren: Leben als kosmologische Zwangsläufigkeit*, Reinbek bei Hamburg, 1997.

Deissler, Alfons. "Biblische Schöpfunsgeschichte und physikalische Kosmologie" in *Vom Anfang der Welt*, ed. J. Audretsch and K. Mainzer, Munich, 1990, 176–87.

Ditfurth, Hoimar von. *Wir sind nicht nur von dieser Welt*, Hamburg, 1981.

Dohmen, Christoph. *Schöpfung und Tod: Dei Entfaltung theologischer und anthropologischer Konzeptionen in Gen 2–3*, SBB 35, Stuttgart, 1996.

Dorschner, Johan, Michael Heller, and Wolfhart Pannenberg. *Menschund Universum. Naturwissenschaft und Schöpfungsglaube im Dialog*, Regensburg, 1995.

Drewermann, Eugen. *Strukturen des Bösen*. Band I: *Die jahwistische Urgeschichte in exegetischer Sicht*, PaThSt 4, Paderborn, 1979; Band 2: *Die jahwistische Urgeschichte in psychoanalytischer Sicht*, PaThSt 5, Paderborn, 1980; Band 3: *Die jahwistische Urgeschichte in philosophischer Sicht*, PaThSt 6, Paderborn, 1980.

Dürr, Hans-Peter, ed. *Physik und Transzendenz: Die großen Physiker unseres Jahrhundert über ihre Begegnung mit dem Wunderbaren*, Bern/Munich/Vienna, 1990.

———, et al. *Gott, der Mensch und die Wissenschaft*, Augsburg, 1997.

Ebach, Jürgen. "Bild Gottes und Schrecken der Tiere: Zur Anthropologie der priesterlichen Urgeschichte," in ders. *Ursprung und Ziel*, Neukirchen-Vluyn, 1986, 16–47.

———. "Schöpfung in der hebräischen Bibel," in *Okologische Theologie: Perspektiven zur Orientierung*, ed. Günter Altner, Stuttgart, 1989, 98–129.

Eccles, John C. *Das Rätsel Mensch*, Munich/Basel, 1982.

———, and Daniel N. Robinson. *Das Wunder des Menschseins—Gehirn und Geist*, Munich/Zürich, 1991.

Eibl-Eibesfeldt, Irenäus. *Die Biologie des menschlichen verhaltens: Grundriß der Humantheologie*, Munich, 1995.

Eliade, Mircea, ed. *Schöpfungsmythen*, Düsseldorf, 2002.

Euler, Harald A. "Religion und sexuelle Selektion," in *Darwin und Gott*, ed. U. Lüke, I. Schnakenberg, and G. Souvignier, Darmstadt, 2004, 66–88.

Fahr, Hans Jörg. "Alternativen zur Urknalltheorie: Die Welt als kosmischer Attraktor," in *Kosmologie*, ed. H. A. Müller, Göttingen, 2004, 70–104.

Ferguson, Kitty. *Gottes Freiheit und die Gesetze der Schöpfung*, Düsseldorf u.a., 1996.

Frettlöh, Magdalene L. *Theologie des Segens: Biblische und dogmatische Warhnehmungen*, Gütersloh, 2002.

Fusch, Gotthard, and Hans Kessler, eds. *Gott, der Kosmos und die Freiheit: Biologie, Philosophie und Theologie im Gespräch*, Würzburg, 1996.

Ganoczy, Alexander. *Chaos, Zufall, Schöpfungsglaube: Die Chaos theorie als Herausforderung der Theologie*, Mainz, 1995.

Gertz, Jan Christian. "Bund II," *AT*, RGG I, 1998, 1862–65.

Gese, Hartmut. "Der bewachte Lebensbaum under die Heroe: zwei mythologische Ergänzungen der Quelle J.," in ders. *Vom Sinai zum Zion*, BevTh 64, Munich, 1974, 99–112.

Gestrich, Christoph. *Die Wiederkehr des Glanzes in der Welt: Die christliche Lehre von der Sünde und ihrer Vergebung in gegenwärtiger Bedeutung*, Tübingen, 1989.

Gitt, Werner. *Schuf Gott durch Evolution?* Neuhausen-Stuttgart, 1992.

Goenner, Hubert. "Das Urknallbild des Kosmos: beginnt die Zeit?" in *Kosmologie*, ed. H. A. Müller, Göttingen, 2004, 24–38.

Goodall, Jane. *Ein Herz für Schimpansen*, Reinbek bei Hamburt, 1996.

Gräb, Wilhelm, ed. *Urknall oder Schöpfung: Zum Dialog zwischen Naturwissenschaft und theologie*, Gütersloh, 1995.

Gregersen, Niels Henrik. "Mensch I," *RGG* V, 2002, 1046–52.

Gutsche, Edith, Peter C. Hägele, and Hermann Hafner, eds. *Zur Diskusion um Schöpfung und Evolution: Gesichtspunkte und Materialien zum Gespäch*, Porta-Studien 6, Marburg, 1998.

Härle, Wilfried. *Dogmatik*, Berlin/New York, 1995.

Hawking, Stephen W. *Eine kurze Geschichte der Zeit (A Brief History of Time): Die Suche nach der Uhrkraft des Universums*, Reinbek bei Hamburg, 1988.

Hegel, Georg Wilhelm Friedrich. *Phänomenologie des Geistes*, Frankfurt a.m., 1970.

Heidegger, Martin. *Sein und Zeit*, Tübingen, 1963.

Heim, Karl. *Weltschöpfung und Weltende: Der evangelische Glaube und das Denken der Gegenwart. Grundzüge einer christlichen Lebensanschauung,* Vol. 6, Hamburg, 1952.

Hemminger, Hansjörg, and Wolfgang Hemminger. *Jenseits der Weltbilder: Naturwissenschaft-Evolution-Schöpfung*, Stuttgart, 1991.

Herrmann, Klaus. "Henoch/Henochschriften," *RGG* III, 2000, 1626–29.

Hieke, Thomas. *Die Gealogien der Genesis*, HBS 39, Freiburg i. Br. u.a., 2003.

Hilpert, Konrad, and Gotthold Hasenh. *Schöpfung und Selbstorganisation*, Paderborn u.a., 1999.

Hornung, Eric. *Der eine und die Vielen: Agyptische gottesvorstellungen*, Darmstadt, 1993.

Höver-Johag, Ingeborg. "Tob," *ThWAT* III, 1982, 315–38.

Illies, Joachim. *Der Jahrhundertirrtum: Würdigung und Kritik des Darwinismus*, Frankfurt a.m., 1984.

Janowski, Bernd. "Das biblische Weltbild: Eine methodologische Skizze," in ders. *Das biblische Weltbild und seine altorientalischen Kontexts*, ed. B. Ego, FAT 32, 2001, 3–26, = ders. *Der Gott des Lebens: Beiträge zur Theologie des Alten Testaments* 3, Neukirchen-Vluyn 2003, 3–26.

———. *Das Königtum Gottes in den Psalmen: Bemerkungen zu einem neuen Gesmtenwurf*, ZThK 86, 1989, 389–454, = ders. *Gottes Gegenwart in Israel: Beiträge zur Theologie des Alten Testaments*, Neukirchen-Vluyn, 1993, 148–213.

———. "Die heiligen Wohungen des Höchsten: Kosmologische Imlikationen der Jerusalemer Tempeltheologie," in ders. *Der Gott des Lebens*, 27–71.

———. "Herrschaft über die Tiere: Gen 1:26-28 und die Semanitk von," in ders. *Die rettende Gerechtigkeit: Beiträge zur Theologie des Alten Testaments 2*, Neukirchen-Vluyn, 1999, 33–48.

———. "Jenseits von Eden: Gen 4:1-16 und die nicht-prieseterliche Urgeschichte," in *Der Gott des Lebens*, 134–56.

———. "Kain und Abel," *RGG* IV, 2001, 736–37.

———. "Schöpfung," *RGG* VII, 2004, 970–72.

———. *Tempel und Schöpfung: Schöpfungstheologische Aspekte der priesterschriftlichen Heiligtumkonzeption*, JBTh 5, 1990, 37–70, = ders. *Gottes Gegenwart in Israel*, 214–46.

Jantsch, Erich. *Die Selbstorganisation des Universums: Vom Urknall zum menschlichen Geist*, Munich, 1984.

Jeremias, Jörg. *Die reue Gottes*, BSt 65, Neukirchen-Vluyn, 1975, 1997.

———. *Schöpfung in Poesie und Prosa des Alten Testament: Gen 1–3 im Vergleich mit anderen Schöpfungstexten des Alten Testaments*, JBTh 5, 1990, 11–36.

Jeßberger, Rolf. *Kretionisus: Kritik des modernen Antirevolutionismus*, Berlin/Hamburg, 1990.

Jork, Gudrun. "Sexualität—Eine uralte Geschichte (Gen 3)," in *Doppeldeutlich. Tiefendimensionen biblischer Texte*, ed. Y. Speigel, Munich, 1978, 44–58.

Jüngel, Eberhard. *Gott als Geheimnis der Welt*, Tübingen, 1977.

Junker, Reinhard, and Siegfried Scherer. *Evolution: Ein kritisches Lehrbuch*, Gießen, 1998.

Kaiser, Otto. *Text aus der Umwelt des AT (TUAT) III*, 3/4, Gütersloh, 1982.

Kanitschneider, Bernulf. "Naturphilosophie, Kosmologie und das Anthropische Prinzip," in *Vom Anfang der Welt*, ed. J. Audretsch and K. Mainzer, Munich, 1990, 157–75.

———. *Von der mechanistischen Welt zum kreativen Universum*, Darmstadt, 1993.

Kant, Imanuel. "Mutmaßlicher Anfang der Menschheitsgeschichte," in *Werke in 10 Bänden*, Band 9, ed. Vn. W. Weischedel, Darmstadt, 1968, 85–102.

Käsemann, Ernst. *An die Römer*, NHT 8a, Tübingen, 1974.

Keel, Othmar, and Silvia Schroer. *Schöpfung: Biblische Theologien im Kontext altorientalischer Religionen*, Göttingen/Fribourg, 2002.

Kessler, Hans. "Gott, der kosmische Prozess und die Freiheit: Vorentwurf einer transzendental-dialogsichen Schöpfungstheologie," in *Gott, der Kosmos und die Freiheit*, ed. G. Fuchs and H. Kessler, Würzburg, 1996, 189–232.

Kierkegaard, Sören: *Der Begriff Angst (The Concept of Anxiety)*, Werke I, Reinbek bei, Hamburg, 1960.

Knapp, Andreas. *Wie böse ist der "böse Wolf"? Zum Verhältnis von Natur und Moral*, GuL 9, 1994, 141–52.

Knierim, Rolf. *Die Hauptbegriffe für Sünde im Alten Testament*, Gütersloh, 1967.

Koch, Klaus. "Die Toledot-Formeln als Strukturprinzip des Buches Genesis," in *Recht und Ethos im AT—Gestalt und Wirkung* (FS, H. Seebass), Neukirchen-Vluyn, 1999, 183–92.

———. "Gestaltet die Erde, doch heget das Leben! Einige Klarstellungen zum *dominum terrae* in Genesis I," in *Wenn nicht jetzt, wann dann?* (FS, H. J. Kraus), Neukirchen-Vluyn, 1983, 23–36.

———. *Wort und Einheit des Schöpfergottes in Memphis und Jeruslaem*, ZThK 62, 1965, 251–93 = ders. *Studien zur alttestamentlichen und altorientalischen Religionsgeschichte*, Göttingen, 1988, 61–105.

Kratz, Reinhard G., and Hermann Sieckermann. *Artikel Schöpfer/Schöpfung II: Altes Testament*, TRE 30, 1999, 258–83.

Krauss, Heinrich, and Max Küchler. *Erzählungen der Bibel: Das Buch Genesis in literarischer Perspektive: Die biblische Urgeschichte (Gen. 1–11)*, Göttingen u.a., 2003.

Krötke, Wolf, Jörg Hacker, and Dietmar Mieth. *Die Welt als Schöpfung und als Natur*, Neukirchen-Vlyun, 2002.

Krüger, Thomas. "Das menschliche Herz und die Weisung Gottes," in *Rezeption und Auslegung im AT und in seinem Umfeld*, ed. R. G. Kratz and Th. Krüger, OBO 153, Göttingen/Fribourg, 1997, 65–92.

Kutsch, Ernst. *Das posse non peccare und verwandte Formulierungen als Aussage biblischer Theologie*, ZThK 84, 1987, 267–78.

Leakey, Richard, and Lewing, Roger. *Der Ursprung des Menschen*, Auf der S 31, 1993, 56–73.

———. *Uche nach den Spuren des Humanen*, Frankfurt a.m., 2001.

Levin, Christoph. *Der Jahwist*, FRLANT 157, Göttingen, 1993.

———. *Tatbericht und Wortbericht in der preisterschriftlichen Schöpfungserzählung*, ZThK 91, 1994, 115–33.

Lichtenberger, Hermann. *Das Ich Adams und das Ich der Menschheit: Studien zum Menschenbild in Römer 7*, WUNT 164, Tübingen, 2004.

Link, Christian. *Schöpfung: Schöpfungstheologie angesichts der Herausforderungen des 20 Jahrhunderts*, HSTh 7/2, Gütersloh, 1991.

Linke, Bernd Michael, ed. *Schöpfungsmythologie in den Religionen*, Frankfurt a.m., 2001.

Lohfink, Norbert. "Macht euch die Erde untertan?" in *Studien zum Pentateuch*, SBA 4, Stuttgart, 1988, 11–28.

Löning, Karl, and Zenger, Erich. *Als Anfang schuf Gott. Biblische Schöpfungstheologien*, Düsseldorf, 1997.

Lorenz, Konrad. *Das sogenannte Böse: Zur Naturgeschichte der Aggression*, Vienna, 1966.

Lüke, Ulrich. *"Als Angang schuf Gott . . ." Bio-Theologie: Zeit-Evolution-Hominisation*, Paderborn u.a., 1997.

———. *Darwin und Gott: Das Verhältnis von Evolution und Religion*, ed. Jürgen Schnakenberg and Georges Souvignier, Darmstadt, 2004.

———. *Schöpfung als Evolution—Evolution als Schöpfung?* Religionspädagogische, Beiträge 31, 1993, 56–73.

———. "Schöpfung aus dem Nichts oder fortlaufende Schöpfung? Zum Verhältnis von *creatio ex nihilo* und *creatio continua*," in *Kosmologie*, ed. H. A. Müller, Göttingen, 2004, 39–52.

Mathys, Hans-Peter, ed. *Ebenbild Gottes—Herrscher über die Welt*, Studien zur Würde und Auftrag des Menschen, BThSt 33, Neukirchen-Vluyn, 1998.

Miller, Kenneth R. *Finding Darwin's God: A Scientist's Search for Common Ground between God and Evolution*, New York, 1999.

Mohr, Hans. *Natur und Moral: Ethik in der Biologie*, Dimensionen der modernen Biologie 4, Darmstadt, 1987.

Moltmann, Jürgen. *Gott in der Schöpfung: Eine ökologische Schöpfungslehre*, Munich, 1985.

———. "Menschenbild zwischen Evolution und Schöpfung: Eine ökologische Schöpfungslehre," in *Okologische Theologie*, ed. G. Altener, Stuttgart, 1989, 196–212.

Monod, Jacques. *Zufall und Notwendigkeit*, Munich, 1971.

Moran, William L. *The Most Magic Word: Essays on Babylonian and Biblical Literature*, CBQ, MS 35, Washington, DC, 2002.

Mosis, Rudolf. "Biblische Schöpfungsaussagen und heutiges Selbstverständnis der Menschen," in *Schöpfung und Evolution*, ed. K. Schmitz-Moormann, Düsseldorf, 1992, 58–75.

Müller, Hans-Peter. *Mythos—Kerygma—Wahrheit*, BZAW 200, Berlin/New York, 1991.

———. *Schöpfungsmythen—literarisch und theologisch—mit Anschlusserörterungen*, ZThK 101, 2004, 506–25.

Müller, Helmut A., ed. *Kosmologie: Evolution und Eschatologie der Welt*, RThN 2, Göttingen, 2004.

Mutschler, Hans-Dieter. "Die Welterklärung der Physik und die Lebenswelt des Menschen," in *Urknall oder Schöpfung?* ed. W. Gräb, Gütersloh, 1995, 43–62.

———. *Physik, religion, New Age*, Würzburg, 1990.

Neumann-Gorsolke, Ute. *Herrschen in den Grenzen der Schöpfung: Ein Beitrag zur alttestamentlichen Anthropologie am Beispiel von Psalm 8, Genesis 1, und verwandten Texten*, WMANT 101, Neukirchen-Vluyn, 2004.

Ohlig, Karl-Heinz. *Religion in der Geschichte der Menschheit*, Darmstadt, 2002.

Otto, Eckhardt. "Pentateuch," *RGG*, IV, 2003, 1089–102.

———. "Woher weiß der Mensch um Gut und Böse? Philosophische Annäherungen der ägyptischen und biblischen Weisheit an ein grundproblem der Ethik," in *Recht und Ethos im AT: Testalt und Wirkung* (FS, H. Seebass), ed. S. Beyerle, G. Mayer, and H. Strauß, Neukirchen-Vluyn, 1999, 201–31.

Pagels, Elaine. *Adam, Eva und die Schlange: Die Theologie der Sünder*, Reinbek bie Hamburg, 1991.

Pannenberg, Wolfhart. *Aggression und die theologische Lehre von der Sünde*, ZEE 21, 1977, 161–73.

———. "Die Frage nach Gott als Schöpfer der Welt und die neuere Kosmologie," in *Kosmologie*, ed. H. A. Müller, Göttingen, 2004, 197–208.

———. *Systematische Theologie*, Vol. 2, Göttingen, 1991.

Peacocke, Arthur R. *Gottes Wirken in der Welt: Theologie im Zeitalter der Naturwissenschaften*, Mainz, 1998.

———. "Natur und Gott: Für eine Theologie im Zeitalter der Wissenschaft," in *Gott, Der Kosmos, und die Freiheit*, ed. G. Fuchs and H. Kessler, Würzburg, 1996, 170–88.

———. *Paths from Science to God*, Oxford, 2002.

Peters, Ted, and Martinez Hewlett. *Evolution from Creation to New Creation: Conflict, Conversation, and Convergence*, Nashville, 2003.

Polkinghorne, John. *An Gott glauben im Zeitalter der Naturwissenshaftern: Die Theologie eines Physikers*, Gütersloh, 2000.

———. *Theologie und Naturwissenschaften: Eine Einführung*, Gütersloh, 2001.

Prigogine, Ilya, and Isabelle Stengers. *Dialog mit der Natur: Neue Wege naturwissenschaftlichen Denkens*, Munich/Zürich, 1993.

Rad, Gerhard von. *Das erste Buch Mose, Genesis*, ATD 1, Göttingen, 1949, 1987.

———. "Das theologische Problem des alttestmentlichen Schöpfungsglaubens," (1936), in ders. *Student zum Alten Testament*, TB 8, Munich, 1971, 136–47.

———. *Theologie des Alten Testaments*. Band 1: *Die Theologie der geschichtlichen Uberlieferungen Israels*, Munich, 1957.

Rahner, Karl. "Naturwissenschaft und vernüftiger Glaube," in ders. *Wissenschaft und christlicher Glaube*, Schriften zur Theologie 15, Zürich u.a., 1983, 24–62.

Rendtorff, Rolf. *Theologie des Alten Testaments*. Band 2: *Thematische Entfaltung*, Neukirchen-Vluyn, 2001.

Richter, Horst Eberhard. *Der Gotteskomplex: Die Geburt und die Krise des Glaubens an die Allmacht des Menschen*, Reinbek bie Hamburg, 1986.

Rüterswörden, Udo. *Dominium terrae*, BZAW 215, Berlin/New York, 1993.

Sattler, Dorothea, and Theodor Schneider. "Schöpfungslehre," in *Handbuch der Dogmatik*, Band 1, ed. Th. Schneider, Düsseldorf, 1995, 120–240.

Schmid, Hans Heinrich. *Gerechtigkeit als Weltordnung*, BHTh 40, Tübingen, 1968.

———. "Schöpfung, Gerechtigkeit, und Heil: Schöpfungstheologie als Gesamthorizont biblischer Theologie," in ders. *Altorientalische Welt in der alttestamentlichen Theologie*, Zürich, 1974, 9–37.

Schmidt, Ludwig. "Pentateuch," in *Neukirchener Arbeitsbücher AT*, ed. Hans Jochen Boecker, Neukirchen, 1996, 80–100.

———. *Schöpfung: Natur und Geschichte*, 246–89.

Schmidt, Werner H. *Alttestamentlicher Glaube in seiner Geschichte*, Neukirchen-Vluyn, 1996.

———. "Br'schaffen," *THAT* 1, 1971, 336–39.

———. *Die Schöpfungsgeschichte der Preiesterschrift*, WMANT 17, Neukirchen-Vluyn 1967.

———. "Schöpfung im Alten Testament," in *Verstehen—Bewahren—Gestalten*, ed. J. Track and Ch. Link, Neukirchen-Vluyn, 2003, 63–83.

Schmitz-Moormann, Karl. *Materie-Leben-Geist: Evolution als Schöpfung Gottes*, Mainz, 1997.

———, ed. *Schöpfung und Evolution: Neue Ansätze zum Dialog zwischen Naturwissenschaft und Theologie*, Düsseldorf, 1992.

Schockenhoff, Eberhard, and Max G. Huber, eds. *Gott und der Urknall. Physikalische Kosmologie und Schöpfungsglaube*, Freiburg i. Br/Munich, 2004.

Schottroff, W. "jd'/erkennen," *THAT* 1, 682–701.

Schwarz, Hans. *Schöpfungsglaube im Horizont moderner Naturwissenschaft*, Konstanz, 1996.

Seebass, Horst. *Genesis I, Urgeschichte (1-11, 26)*, Neukirchen-Vluyn, 1996.

———. "Jahwist," *TRE* 16, 1987, 441–51.

———. "Pentateuch," *TRE* 26, 1996, 185–209.

Smend, Rudolf. *Die Entstehung des Alten Testaments*, ThW I, Stuttgart u.a., 1989.

Soden, Wolfram von. "Der Mensch bescheidet sich nicht: Uberlegungen zu Schöpfungserzählungen in Babylonien und Israel," in *Bibel und Alter Orient: Altorientalische Beiträge zum AT*, ed. V. H.-P. Müller, Berlin/New York, 1985, 165–73.

———. "Etemenanki vor Asarhaddon nach der Erzählung vom Turmbau zu Babel und dem Erra-Mythos," in *Bibel und Alter Orient*, 134–47.

Söding, Thomas, ed. *Ist der Glaube Feind der Freiheit? Die neue Debatte um den Monotheismus*, QD 196, Freiburg i. Br. u.a., 2003.

Sommer, Volker. "Das Töten von Artgenossen," in *Die zehn Geobte*, ed. H. Albertz, Stuttgart, 1987, 85–97.

———, and Karl Amann. *Die großen Menschenaffen: Neue Sicht der Verhaltensforschung*, Munich, 1998.

Spieckermann, Hermann. *Heilsgegenwart: Eine Theologie der Psalmen*, FRLANT 148, Göttingen, 1989.

Stadelmann, Hans-Rudolf. *Im Herzen der Materie: Glaube im Zeitalter der Naturwissenschaften*, Darmstadt, 2004.

Steck, Odil Hannes. *Die Paradieserzählung: Eine Auslegung von Genesis 2:43–3:24*, BSt 60, Neukirchen-Vluyn, 1970.

————. *Der Schöpfungsbericht der Priesterschrift: Studien zur literarkritischen und überlieferungsgeschichtlichen Problematik von Genesis 1:1–2:4a*, FRLANT 115, Göttingen, 1981.

————."Genesis 12, 1-3 und die Urgeshcichte des Jahwisten," 1971, in ders. *Wahrnehmnungen Gottes im Alten Testament*, Gesammelte Studien, TB 70, Munich, 1982, 117–48.

————. *Welt und Umwelt: Biblische Konfrontationen*, Stuttgart u.a., 1978.

Stoebe, Hans-Joachim. "Hamas/Gewalttat," *THAT* I, 1971, 583–87.

————. "tob/gut," *THAT* I, 1971, 652–64.

Stolz, Fritz. *Einführung in den biblischen Monotheismus*, Darmstadt, 1996.

Trefil, James S. *Im Augenblick der Schöpfung: Physik des Urknalls: Von der Planck-Zeit bis heute*, Basel u.a., 1984.

Uehlinger, Christoph. *Weltreich und "eine Rede": Eine neue Deutung der sogenannten Turmbauerzählung (Gen 11:1-9)*, OBO 101, Göttingen/Fribourg, 1990.

Victorri, Bernhard. *Die Debatte um die Urspraceh: Spectrum der Wissenschaft*, Dossier, o.j., 16–19.

Vogel, Christian. *Vom Töten zum Mord: Das wirklich Böse in der Evolutionsgeschichte*, Munich/Vienna, 1989.

Voland, Eckart, and Söling, Caspar. "Die biologische Basis der Religiositätin Instinkten," in *Darwin und Gott*, ed. U. Lüke, J. Schnakenberg, and G. Souvignier, Darmstadt, 2004, 47–65.

Vollmert, Bruno. *Das Molekül und das Leben*, Reinbek bei Hamburg, 1985.

Wandrey, Irina. "Noachidische Gebote," *RGG* IV, 2003, 348–49.

Weckwerth, Gerd. "Das anthropische Prinzip in der Entwicklung unseres Kosmos," in *Kosmologie*, ed. H. A. Müller, Göttingen, 2004, 53–70.

Wegter-McNelly, Kirk. "Quantenphysik," *RGG* IV, 2003, 1858–59.

Weidemann, Volker. "Die Entstehung der Welt aus dem Nichts: Kosmologie an den Grenzen der Naturwissenschaft," in *Zur Kritik der wissenschaftlichen Rationalität* (FS, K. Hübner), ed. H. Lenk, Freiburg i. Br., 1986, 467–85.

Weinberg, Steven. *Der Traum von der Einheit des Universums*, Munich, 1995.

————. *Die ersten drei Minuten: Der Ursprung des Universums*, Munich, 1997.

Weingartner, Paul, ed. *Evolution als Schöpfung? Ein Streitgespräch zwischen Philosophen, Theologen, und Naturwissenschaftlern*, Stuttgart u.a., 2001.

Weissmahr, Béla. "Evolution als Offenbarun der freiheitlichn Dimension der Wirklichkeit," in *Kann man Gott aus der Natur erkennen?* ed. C. Bresch, Freiburg i.Br. u.a., 1992, 87–101.

Welker, Michael. *Schöpfung: Big Bang oder Siebentagewerk?* GuL 9, 1994, 126–40.

————. *Schöpfung und Wirklichkeit*, NBSTh 13, Neukirchen-Vluyn, 1995.

Werbick, Jürgen. "Absolutistischer Eingottglaube? Befrieiende Vielfalt des Polytheismus?" in *Ist der Glaube Feind der Freiheit?* ed. Th. Söding, Freiburg i.Br. u.s., 2003, 142–75.

Westermann, Claus. *Genesis I.* Teilband *Genesis 1–11*, BKAT I/1, Neukirchen-Vluyn, 1983.

————. *Genesis 1–11*, EdF 7, Darmstadt, 1972.

————. *Schöpfung*, TT 12, Stuttgart u.a., 1971.

———. *Welt und Mensch im Urgeschehen: Die biblische Urgeshichte (1 Mose 1–11)*, Stuttgart, 1999.

Whitcomb, John C., and Henry M. Morris. *Die Sintflut*, Neuhausen-Stuttgart, 1977.

Whitehead, Alfred North. *Prozess und Realität: Entwurf einer Kosmologie*, Frankfurt a.m., 1984.

Wickler, Wolfgang. *Die Biologie der 10 Gebote*, Munich/Zürich, 1991.

———, and Uta Seibt. *Das Prinzip Eigennutz: Zur Evolution sozialen Verhalten*, Munich/Zürich, 1993.

Wilder Smith, Amos. *Die Naturwissenschaften kennen keine Evolution*, Basel, 1978.

Wilken, Ulrich. *Der Brief an die Römer (Rom 1–5)*, EKK VI/1, Neukrichen-Vluyn, 1997.

Wilson, Edward O. *Biologie als Schicksal*, Frankfurt a.m., 1980.

———. *Die Einheri des Wissens*, Munich, 2000.

Winder, Urs. "Der Lebensbaum im Alten Testament und die Ikonographie des stiliserten Baums in Kanaan/Israel," in *Das Kleid der Erde: Pflanzen in der Lebenswelt des alten Israel*, ed. U. Neumann-Gorsolke and P. Rieder, Stuttgart/Neukirchen-Vluyn, 2002, 138–68.

Witte, Markus. *Die biblische Urgeschichte: Redaktions—und theologiegeschichtliche Beobachtungen zur Endredaktion zur Genesis 1:1–11:26*, BZAW 265, Berlin/New York, 1998.

Wolff, Hans Walter. "Das Kerygma des Jahwisten," 1964, in ders. *Gesammelte Studien zum AT*, TB 22, Munich, 1973, 345–73.

Woolley, Leonard. *Ur in Chaldea*, Wiesbaden, 1957.

Wuketits, Franz M. *Evolutionstheorien: Historische Voraussetzungen, Positionene, Kritik*, Dimensionen der modernen Biologie 7, Darmstadt, 1988.

———. *Verdammt zur Unmoral? Zur Naturgeschichte von Gut und Böse*, Munich, 1993.

Zenger, Erich, ed. *Einleitung in das Alter Testament*, Stuttgart, 2001.

———. *Gottes Bogen in den Wolken: Untersuchungen zur Komposition und Theologie der preisterschriftlichen Urgeschichte*, SBS 112, Stuttgart, 1983.

———. "Priesterschrift," *TRE* 27, 1997, 435–46.

Ziegler, Bernhard. *Der schwäbische Lindwurm: Funde aus der Urzeit*, Stuttgart, 1986.

Zwickel, Wolfgang. "Keniter," *CBL* I, 2003, 728–29.

Index

Index

Index

Priesthood, xiii, 92, 134, 139
Process theology, 58
Psychology, deep, 41

Quantum physics, 53, 58

Report of deed/word, 4, 7

Selection, 22, 143
Sexuality, 30, 34, 41, 65
Shame, xv, 31, 34
Sin, origins of, 44, 81
Sin and guilt, xv, 39, 40–45, 48–49, 67–69, 75, 139–40

Source documents, xiii, 92
Standard model, 52

Theodicy, 20, 58, 63
Theogony, 2, 19
Tiamat, 3, 5, 18
Toledot, formula of, 13, 23, 80, 83, 95, 119, 124
Torah, xiv, 61
Trust, origin of, 31, 61, 76, 118
Tsunami, 115

Wisdom, 39
World view, 6, 60, 72

178